TAKE HER, SHE'S MINE

ARRIVALS

FLIGHT NO.	DUE TO ARRIVE	WILL ARRIVE	GATE	FROM
23	935		6	DALLAS
127	950		7	CHICAGO
105	1000		4	PHOENIX
37	1025		5	SAN DIEGO
417	1030		6	HOUSTON
611	1040		5	DETROIT

DEPAR[TURES]

FLIGHT NO.	DUE TO DEPART	WILL DEPART	GAT[E]
628	920		4
34	930		
36	1030		
218	1040		
606			

Take Her, She's Mine

A comedy

by Phoebe and
Henry Ephron

Random House
New York

TAKE HER, SHE'S MINE *was first presented by Harold S. Prince at the Biltmore Theatre, New York City, on December 21, 1961, with the following cast:*

(IN ORDER OF APPEARANCE)

PRINCIPAL	Nicholas Saunders
FRANK MICHAELSON	Art Carney
ANNE MICHAELSON	Phyllis Thaxter
MOLLIE MICHAELSON	Elizabeth Ashley
LIZ MICHAELSON	June Harding
EMMETT WHITMYER	Stephen Paley
AIRPORT CLERK	Ron Welsh
ADELE McDOUGALL	Jean McClintock
SARAH WALKER	Louise Sorel
DONN BOWDRY	Tom Brannum
1ST FRESHMAN	Marty Huston
2ND FRESHMAN	Ron Welsh
RICHARD GLUCK	Walter Moulder
ALFRED GREIFFINGER	Paul Geary
ALEX LOOMIS	Richard Jordan
MR. WHITMYER	Heywood Hale Broun
LINDA LEHMAN	Susan Stein
CLANCY SUSSMAN	Joe Ponazecki
MR. HIBBETTS	Ferdi Hoffman

Directed by George Abbott

Scenery and lighting by William and Jean Eckart

Costumes by Florence Klotz

SYNOPSIS

The action of the play takes place in Southern California and New England.

ACT ONE

A year ago.

ACT TWO

Now.

TAKE HER, SHE'S MINE

ACT ONE

Time: A year ago.

Scene: The stage is divided into several playing areas, all very flexible and indicated by a few light portable props. At the extreme left, a telephone pole carries a tangle of telephone wires across the stage, quite high up, to connect with another telephone pole, stage right. Stage right is Southern California, where the Michaelson family lives, and stage left is the East, where MOLLIE *goes to college. From time to time, as indicated in the action, the Michaelson living room appears at right and the dormitory room appears at left. Center stage is a general playing area which varies in nature by the use of small backdrops or appropriate props. Whenever the action shifts from one portion of the stage to another, the lights go out on the section of the stage not being used. This direction is not to be repeated in the course of the play, but is taken for granted. The back wall is a sky drop.*

At rise: A high school graduation is going on, stage center. A man who looks like a school PRINCIPAL *is handing out imaginary diplomas to imaginary girls and boys, whose names he calls out. On a step slightly above him and to one side is* MOLLIE MICHAELSON, *in white cap and gown. As each name is called,* MOLLIE *moves one step to the side, closer to the* PRINCIPAL, *preparatory to coming down the step and receiving her diploma.* MOLLIE *is almost eighteen, intelligent, alert, enthusiastic, with the look of a young woman who has had everything proper—from tooth-straightening to dancing classes—done for*

3

her. The rest of the Michaelson family—FRANK, ANNE *and* LIZ—*are seated to one side, watching the ceremony.* FRANK *and* ANNE *are an attractive couple in their early forties and very young-looking. Their daughter* LIZ *is about fifteen, still gangly and awkward, but showing promise that she will one day be a beauty.*

PRINCIPAL (*Reading from a list*) Dorothy Lewkins . . .

> (*The imaginary Dorothy Lewkins is handed an imaginary diploma, and the* PRINCIPAL *pantomimes a handshake.* MOLLIE *moves one step closer, as there is a spatter of applause.* MOLLIE *looks at the family and smiles*)

Judith Markowitz . . . (*He offers another imaginary diploma*) Frederick Arthur Meadows, Jr., Fidelis Award.

> (*Another diploma, with a little more enthusiastic applause.* MOLLIE *is now next*)

Mollie Michaelson . . .

> (*He offers her her diploma. The* PRINCIPAL *pauses impressively, as* MOLLIE *comes down the step to him, smiling a delightfully wide smile*)

Ephebian, Sealbearer, Fidelis Award—and now receiving the Gold Cord for Scholarship.

> (*He drapes the imaginary gold cord around* MOLLIE'S *neck, shakes her hand, and she exits, as the audience, especially the Michaelsons, are heard applauding enthusiastically. As the lights dim out* FRANK *walks to the proscenium, stage left, and looks out at the audience*)

FRANK That's my daughter. When it's your own daughter, and she gets all those . . . (*Emotion makes him stop for a moment, to collect himself*) I had some idea of how the President's mother and father felt the day he was inaugurated. That may be a somewhat exaggerated comparison. Still I don't think you have to be too modest. After all, only eighteen years ago—seventeen and a half to be exact—we brought home from the hospital a five-pound bundle no bigger than a chicken you get at the supermarket—and there was that five-pound bundle up there with a smile on her face that would . . . (*Breaks off again*) Anyway, it's quite clear that we've got a "Brain." And that imposes an obligation on you. Now, more than ever, the world is being shaped by ideas. And Mollie might just possibly be one of those people who . . . (*Stops, and comes down to earth*) So we were very pleased when Mollie got into a good Eastern college. As a matter of fact she had her choice of four. She elected to go to Hawthorne College for Women. Hawthorne College has a student body of two thousand. It is located in Massachusetts, and it's bounded on the east by the Atlantic Ocean, on the west by Harvard, on the north by Dartmouth, and on the south by Yale. It's supposed to be a good location. Well, I won't bore you with what it costs to send a child to college these days. I'll only tell you it comes to a little more than twice what Annie and I lived on the first year we were married. But I'm not complaining. I can afford it. I got into plastics early. I've done very well. Mollie isn't the "Brain" by accident. There's *something* to be said for the genes. (*He beams at himself and the world*) Anyway, we'll have an extra expense. We live in Southern California so about four times a year we'll find ourselves at the Los Angeles International Airport. I don't know about you, but I'll never get used to airplane travel. It's not so bad when you're going by yourself. You're too busy to be nervous. But when you're seeing somebody else off, and she's not quite eighteen years old, and it's the first time . . . We-ell . . .

(FRANK *exits. At center stage, an American Airlines Arrival and Departure sign appears. Various flight num-*

bers and times are indicated on it. MOLLIE, ANNE *and*
LIZ *enter and look up at the sign.* ANNE *and* LIZ *are
dressed California style, rather casually.* MOLLIE *is wearing a traveling suit and hat. She carries a coat over one
arm and a book and some magazines in her other arm.*
ANNE *carries another coat and a small dressing case.* LIZ
*holds a box of cookies, and a large shapeless bag, stuffed
to capacity. She sets the bag down. No one but our
principals will be seen in this scene, but there is a
hubbub of voices and the muted sound of planes taking
off and arriving)*

ANNE What's the number of your flight, Mollie?

MOLLIE Thirty-six.

LIZ Gate Seven—it's on time.

ANNE I'm sure I should have something profound to say to
you—but I can't for the life of me think what.

MOLLIE Don't worry, Mom. Daddy will have something profound to say to me.

LIZ Well, this isn't very deep, but I'll miss you, Mollie.

MOLLIE Me too, Liz.
 (*The two girls kiss.* ANNE *starts to sniffle*)

ANNE I'm going to cry.

MOLLIE For heaven's sake, Mom, you cried all through the
packing. (*She waves to somebody evidently going past*) Hi,
Lucy! You on Flight Thirty-six? (*The answer is apparently
affirmative*) Good! See you on the plane.

6

ANNE (*Watching the non-existent Lucy's departure*) Who's Lucy?

MOLLIE Lucy Shanks. She's going to Smith.

ANNE She's wearing that suit you tried on at Magnin's.

MOLLIE Well, now will you admit I didn't make a mistake?
(FRANK *enters, looking as if he has been running*)

FRANK Where the hell have you been? I've been looking all over the airport for you.

MOLLIE (*Crossing to* FRANK) Daddy, I'm traveling American Airlines. We're right in front of the counter. Where else would we be?

FRANK Oh. (*A small voice*) I thought it was United.

ANNE Calm down, dear.
(ANNE *joins* LIZ, *leaving* FRANK *and* MOLLIE *together*)

FRANK Checked in, Mollie?

MOLLIE Yes, Daddy.

FRANK Good seat?

MOLLIE By the window.

FRANK Any overweight?

MOLLIE No.
(FRANK *looks at* MOLLIE, *love and affection shining in his eyes. He puts his hands on* MOLLIE's *shoulders.* ANNE *and* LIZ *exchange looks of "he's off again," and stand back and listen*)

FRANK Now listen, Mollie, you're being given a great opportunity. It isn't every girl who gets it. Not that you haven't
earned it. But, in its own way, Hawthorne is in a class with
great schools like Harvard, Yale, Oxford. Now you've got
the mind to take this opportunity and . . .
(*He breaks off as* MOLLIE *spots somebody over his
shoulder and waves gaily*)

MOLLIE Hi, Roger! You on Flight Thirty-six? (*Waits for an
answer*) Good! See you on the plane.
(*All except* FRANK *watch the departure of the non-
existent Roger*)

ANNE Who's that?

MOLLIE (*Crossing to* ANNE) Roger Ezor. He got into Dartmouth—to everybody's surprise, including his own.

FRANK Mollie . . .

MOLLIE (*Obediently; goes back to* FRANK) Yes, Daddy. I have
a very fine mind and a very fine opportunity.

FRANK Well, what I mean is, make use of it. Make use of it
to the fullest extent. So that in later years you won't feel
that you wasted a great opportunity and we won't feel that
all this money is going just for . . . (*He sees the enormous
bag behind* MOLLIE *and stops short*) That bag! I thought
you were checked through.

MOLLIE I'm taking that on the plane with me.
(FRANK *goes to bag, picks it up and feels its weight*)

FRANK Are you crazy? They won't let you get away with that.

MOLLIE (*With great patience*) Will you please stop worrying,
Daddy? Anybody who weighs as little as I do shouldn't

8

have to pay overweight. (*Whispers*) Look at that man—(*Indicates; all look*)—two hundred and fifty pounds if he weighs an ounce. Is he being charged for his overweight?

FRANK But suppose they don't let you through with that?

MOLLIE They won't even see it. After I'm through the gate all you have to do is hand it to me over the fence. (FRANK *drops the bag with a thud*) It's common practice. (*Waves to someone*) Hi, Joycie. Hello, Mr. and Mrs. Kincaid. (*Joycie and the Kincaids have evidently stopped*) I'd like you to meet my parents—and my sister, Elizabeth. (FRANK, ANNE *and* LIZ *all murmur* "*How do you do*") Joycie is going to Hawthorne, too.
 (ANNE *and* FRANK *warm up genially in the presence of these equally fortunate parents*)

ANNE Well, how nice.

MOLLIE (*Moves to stage left, confines her remarks to Joyce*) Joycie, what do you think? Roger broke off with Alice! . . . Right after Brenda's party . . . Well, it never would have lasted anyway, what with her going to Cal and him at Dartmouth.
 (*She laughs*)

ANNE I suppose we'll be seeing a lot of each other in the next four years.

FRANK At the airport, anyway. (*Listens to something Mr. Kincaid is evidently saying*) Yes, I guess we *can* be very proud of them.

MOLLIE Say, you'd better hurry. Most of the good seats are gone already.

FRANK   Very nice to have met you, too. We'll look forward to seeing you again—er—just before Christmas. (*He is beaming as the Kincaids leave*) Now what was I talking about?

LIZ   The challenge of the future.
>   (MOLLIE *comes back to* FRANK)

FRANK   Oh, yes. (*Pulls himself together*) Look, Mollie, you can go to college and just have a good time. Lots of people do it and there isn't anything really wrong with it. But these are the times . . .
>   (MOLLIE *suddenly remembers something, and smites herself on the brow*)

MOLLIE   (*Crossing to Liz*)   Liz! I forgot my black strapless bra. It's on my dresser.

LIZ   (*Cutting in*)   If you're the smartest one in this family, why do you always forget everything?

FRANK   (*Also cutting in*)   Mollie, I'm trying to tell you something that's vital.

MOLLIE   (*Without looking at him*)   Yes, Daddy. Now Liz, there are three dresses that absolutely *need* that bra, so you won't forget to send it to me, will you?

FRANK   (*With a subdued roar*)   *I'll* send you the black strapless bra if you'll just listen to me! (*This brings everybody around.* MOLLIE *marches back to stand and face her father.* FRANK *gets set to go into his speech again. They haven't seen him yet, but* EMMETT WHITMYER *has entered stage left, behind* FRANK. EMMETT *is a gangling young man, attired in jeans and a T-shirt and scuffed sneakers. He is hopelessly in love with* MOLLIE) Now, Mollie, you're taking a very important step in your life. These are the times—

EMMETT (*Coming closer*) That try men's souls.
   (*They all turn and look at him*)

FRANK Oh. Hello, Paul.

MOLLIE Not Paul, Daddy. Emmett.

FRANK Emmett. Where are you going?

EMMETT I'm not going any place, Mr. Michaelson. I just came
down to say good-bye to Mollie.

MOLLIE (*Crosses to* EMMETT; *a bit patronizingly*) Emmett,
that's so dear.

EMMETT Er . . . er . . . I wasn't sure you'd be glad to see me.
   (FRANK *takes a great interest in the conversation*)

MOLLIE But of course I'm glad to see you. What makes you
think that?
   (ANNE *takes in the situation*)

ANNE Frank (*Gestures him away*), I want Mollie to take a
Dramamine before she gets on the plane. Let's go find a
Coke machine. Come on, Liz.
   (*They start off.* EMMETT *is gazing at* MOLLIE, *a woebe-
gone look on his face.* FRANK *looks back curiously*)

FRANK I know my mind isn't attuned to subtleties, but are
they . . . ?
   (*He stops*)

ANNE It's all on his side. He's a terribly bright boy, really
quite desirable, but he's a year younger.

LIZ Three months.

ANNE Well, he's a year behind her at school, so it's quite impossible.

FRANK Why?
(ANNE *and* LIZ *look at him as if he has lost his mind*)

LIZ Daddy! When she's a sophomore at college—he'll be a *freshman!* It's just not done.
(*They go off.* MOLLIE *shakes her head at* EMMETT)

MOLLIE Emmett, will you please take that look off your face. I can't stop *living.* (*Puts coat and magazines down*) I have to go on with my life.

EMMETT I can't help what I feel. I brought you something.
(*He holds out a slender volume. She takes it*)

MOLLIE *Sonnets from the Portuguese.* Oh, thank you, Emmett. I just love them.

EMMETT (*Dead earnest*) Elizabeth Barrett Browning was six years older than Robert Browning. (MOLLIE *turns away*) Need I say more?

MOLLIE No.

EMMETT And Beatrice Webb was older than Sidney Webb. And Martha Washington had a year on George!

MOLLIE (*Turns to* EMMETT) Emmett, you're an absolute panic! You're the first person in the world who ever did research for a farewell scene.

EMMETT Will you write to me?

MOLLIE I won't make a promise that I might not keep.

EMMETT (*Overcome*) You mean you won't even *write?*

MOLLIE Emmett, you're a brilliant boy. But it's wrong. Why should I do anything to prolong a relationship that's doomed?

EMMETT All right. I can see how much all of this means to you right now. But mark my words—however much you say "no," however much time and distance separate us— one day you'll realize this is inevitable! Have a good time.
(He starts off, comes right back)

MOLLIE Thank you, Emmett. Good-bye.
(She holds out her hand. He takes it)

EMMETT Good-bye. *(She leans forward as if to kiss him on the cheek. He pulls away, gestures)* Please! None of your passionless kisses for me!
(He stalks off despondently. MOLLIE looks after him a little sadly, but enjoying to some extent the emotional upheaval she has caused)

LOUDSPEAKER VOICE American Airlines Flight Thirty-six now loading at Gate Seven. Passengers for American Airlines Flight Thirty-six please report to Gate Seven.
(In a moment, FRANK, ANNE, and LIZ rush back into scene. ANNE is carrying a Coke in a paper cup)

FRANK Come on, Mollie. Your plane's loading.
(They start to collect Mollie's possessions)

ANNE Here, darling, take a Dramamine. (MOLLIE *downs it*) And leave some Coke. I want your father to take one, too. Here, Frank.
(She hands him a pill and the cup)

LIZ What does that do?

13

FRANK (*Tensely*) It relaxes you! (*He drinks, gives the cup to* ANNE, *and crosses to* MOLLIE) Have we got everything?

MOLLIE (*Counting quickly*) Two coats, one bag, cookies, dressing case, two books, magazines . . . that's eight.

FRANK Eight.

MOLLIE I'm only supposed to have seven.

FRANK Seven.

MOLLIE (*Remembers*) Oh, yes. Emmett gave me a book.

FRANK Your ticket?

MOLLIE Right here.

FRANK (*Picks up the large bag*) Let's go. There's no turning back now.

> (*They all go toward left proscenium, laden down with* MOLLIE'S *possessions. They do a left turn, and come right back on again. As they do this, the arrival and departure sign disappears. In its place is a steel-link fence with a booth at the end, labeled Gate 7. An* AIRPORT CLERK *in an American Airlines uniform is taking tickets from imaginary passengers, stamping them, and waving the passengers through.* MOLLIE *and her family get on the end of the imaginary line, gradually moving step by step toward the gate.* FRANK *is the center of the group. They talk across him and jostle him as they move. The airplane noises are louder, and a wind is blowing. Everybody speaks in a shriek in order to be heard*)

ANNE I thought Emmett came to see you off. What happened to him?

MOLLIE (*Screaming back at her mother over the noise*) Poor boy. I'm afraid I was mean to him.

ANNE Maybe we should save him for Liz.

LIZ (*A very high-pitched shriek*) Thanks, but I'll find my own. Cast-off dresses, yes; cast-off men, go home!

ANNE Well anyway, Mollie, I wish you'd been nicer to him.

MOLLIE Mother, you can't be nice to Emmett. He's too domineering. And to be dominated by a child . . . Well, anyway, I don't see the point to this whole discussion. It's all part of my past.
(FRANK *has been reacting to this feminine chatter with an expression of distaste. Finally raises his voice louder than anybody's*)

FRANK Please! I love you all very dearly, but constantly being surrounded by women and listening to their—

MOLLIE Daddy, you'll be surrounded by one less from now on.
(FRANK *is silent for a moment.* MOLLIE *isn't even gone yet and already he misses her. The airplane noise has grown softer*)

FRANK Yeah. That's right. You'll remember what I told you, Mollie?

MOLLIE Daddy, you've told me many things and I remember all of them.

ANNE Your ticket.
(*All watch as* MOLLIE's *ticket is validated*)

15

FRANK   Well, good-bye.
(*He kisses* MOLLIE. *Then* ANNE *and* LIZ *kiss her too*)

ANNE   'Bye, darling.

MOLLIE   'Bye, Mom. (ANNE *gives her the coat and dressing case. To* LIZ) 'Bye, Kook.
(LIZ *gives her the cookies and magazines*)

LIZ   'Bye, Mol'.
(*Almost completely obscured by her possessions,* MOLLIE *goes through the gate.* LIZ *and* ANNE *move back and wave farewell.* FRANK *stands, completely unaware that he is still carrying* MOLLIE's *large bag.* MOLLIE *hurries to the fence*)

MOLLIE (*Hissing*)   Daddy! (FRANK *looks at her*) Daddy! The bag!
(FRANK *looks down at bag, then looks nervously at the* AIRPORT CLERK, *who continues about his business. Concealing the bag as best he can,* FRANK *sidles to the fence, hands the bag over, and manages to hook it onto* MOLLIE's *arm.* MOLLIE *turns and scuttles toward the plane.* FRANK *takes a deep breath, and then walks out of playing area to left proscenium*)

FRANK   That's the first criminal act I ever committed in my entire lifetime! But, as I said, she has a fine mind and I *did* ask her to use it. (*The steel-link fence disappears, as stage right the Michaelson living room rolls in.* ANNE *is at the extreme right, fixing a drink*) Later that night, I thought to myself—I must be crazy. (*He moves into living room area and talks to* ANNE) What are we doing, taking one of our dearest possessions, encasing it in a missile, and hurling it from one end of the country to the other?

ANNE Shall I fix you one, too?

FRANK Thanks. Suppose all she comes back with is a husband? There are plenty of those around here. California's full of boys. *And* colleges.
  (*He sits on a couch*)

ANNE You're absolutely right. There's no law that says she has to marry somebody from the Ivy League.
  (*She hands* FRANK *his drink*)

FRANK I can see this is going to be a tough four years. (*Holds up his glass*) Well, to Mollie.
  (ANNE *echoes his words, and both drink*)

ANNE (*Thoughtfully, as she sits beside him*) She's not going to miss us at all.

FRANK (*Reciting a set speech*) I know. That means we've done a good job. She's well-adjusted. She doesn't care if she never sees us again. God, what a lot of psychological crap is thrust on the world these days!

ANNE (*After a pause*) Frank, I think we should take up a hobby. This didn't just pop into my head. I've been thinking about us—Mollie at home was a very big part of my life and your life. I don't think we'd have made it without her and Liz.

FRANK Aaah, there was never anybody for me but you, and vice versa.

ANNE A lot of people who love each other don't make it. But that has nothing to do with the fact that you are hopelessly, uncritically, head-over-heels in love with your daughters. And for the greater part of the next four years one of those two shining faces won't be here to greet you every night. That's why I think we ought to find something to do together. Something we could do at night.

FRANK   Are you about to make an indecent proposal?

ANNE (*Smiles*)   Oh, I wasn't going to give *that* up. This is something else. (*A pause*) I think we should go to Arthur Murray's.

FRANK   Arthur Murray's? (*Looks at her as if she's insane*) What on earth for? I don't need dancing lessons. I'm the best dancer in my age group.

ANNE   You never dance Spanish rhythms. I think we should go to Arthur Murray's and learn Spanish rhythms.

FRANK   Annie, do you suppose I want too much for Mollie? I mean, suppose she comes back too smart? A misfit? Somebody who makes the boys feel inferior? I don't want her left on the vine.

ANNE (*Puts her glass down*)   Mollie won't be left on the vine. Now, what about Arthur Murray?

FRANK (*Doesn't hear that. He is wrapped in his own thoughts; gets up and walks downstage*)   You know, it's a form of torture.

ANNE   What?

FRANK   Well . . . the way a daughter gets hold of you. (*Trying to make her understand*) It's . . . it's like adoring some beautiful woman who . . . just tolerates you.

ANNE (*Rises, puts an arm on* FRANK's *shoulder*)   Mollie doesn't just tolerate you. She treats you that way because she's absolutely confident of your love. It's no problem. She knows you're never going to fall in love with anybody else's daughter. (FRANK *still broods*) My God, she's only been gone three hours and you're so . . . so Hamlet! You'll never make it to Christmas. Now what about Arthur Murray?

FRANK I don't have to go the whole four years she's in college, do I?

(They embrace and the lights go out in the living room. MOLLIE's *room at the dorm at college appears stage left. It is night, and* MOLLIE *is in her robe and pajamas, finishing a letter. The main lighting is supplied by a desk lamp, and only a small part of the room is visible.* MOLLIE *pulls the letter out of the typewriter and signs it, speaking as she does so)*

MOLLIE "Love, Mollie." *(Reading what she had already written)* "P.S. I'm the only one in my class still wearing a retainer on her teeth. It's not the kind of thing I care to be individual about. Please ask Dr. Schick if it's essential. If he says yes, I shall probably lose it. P.P.S. I heard Norman Thomas speak last Monday night on disarmament, which he naturally regards as absolutely necessary, and isn't the world situation just abysmal? Sometimes I think it won't last another week—and here I am still a virgin."

(She had apparently run out of space on the P.S.'s and had written around the margins, making it necessary for her to turn the letter as she reads. She puts the letter down and starts to address the envelope. Lights appear again in the Michaelson living room. FRANK, *in slacks and a sport shirt, comes into room, picks up chair, holds it over his head, and starts to practice the rhumba, counting to himself. The purpose of the chair is to keep*

his shoulders from moving. He goes slowly across the room, shifting his weight cautiously from one foot to the other. LIZ *comes down the steps and watches her father, mouth slightly open*)

LIZ   What the hell are you doing, Daddy?

FRANK (*Lowers chair*)   I'm practicing the rhumba.
(ANNE *enters with a small bowl of fruit and a clean ashtray*)

ANNE (*To* LIZ)   And watch your language.

LIZ   The rhumba?

FRANK (*Without stopping his workout*)   You see, the rhumba has anthropological roots. It didn't begin as a dance.

LIZ (*Moves downstage right, to watch*)   It's not ending as one, either.

FRANK (*Imperturbably*)   Nevertheless, its cultural origins derive from the native carriers moving through the jungle in Africa. This chair represents the burdens they carried on their heads. As they walked, they had to *feel* their way. They couldn't look down. Often the footing was treacherous . . . (*He reaches one foot forward cautiously to demonstrate*) Then, having found firm ground, they shifted their weight and moved with the other foot. (*He shifts weight to the forward foot, achieving an accompanying hip gyration, and extends his other foot*) Did you get that hip movement?

LIZ   That the way they teach the rhumba at Arthur Murray's?

FRANK   I'm getting special attention. The instructor has taken a fancy to me.

LIZ She has?

FRANK *He* has. (*He and* ANNE *laugh*) Well, your mother thought I ought to have a hobby, and this is it.

LIZ The mailman.
  (*She runs off*)

FRANK Hey, Annie, do you remember how you're supposed to turn?
  (*He tries to turn around, gets hopelessly tangled in his own feet*)

ANNE Take a rest, Frank. Let that chair become a chair again.
  (*He puts the chair back.* LIZ *returns, a packet of letters in her hands. She riffles through them*)

LIZ Letter from Mollie!

ANNE How wonderful.

FRANK (*Taking the letter and tearing it open*) It's about time.
  (*He settles himself beside* ANNE *on the couch.* LIZ *sits on a hassock. She and* ANNE *wait expectantly. After a moment, it is quite obvious that he has completely forgotten about them and is absorbed in the letter*)

ANNE Read the letter, darling.
  (FRANK *comes to with a start, and reads*)

FRANK "Dear Family, this is the first chance I've had to write. For days now I've been oriented, registered, examined—by the way, I have poor posture, but so does everyone else apparently—indexed, filed, everything but fingerprinted. I've even had my diction analyzed, and for some reason it came out New Jersey. Can you explain that?"

ANNE   That's ridiculous. She's never been east of the Mississippi.

LIZ   (*Rises and crosses to the sofa*)   You were born in New York, Daddy. She probably caught it from you.

FRANK   What's wrong with her speech, anyway? What's the matter with those people?

ANNE   They didn't say anything was wrong with her speech. They just said it was New Jersey. Will you go on with the letter?

FRANK   (*Reading*)   "But enough of that. Our room is just fabulous, now that Adele and I have it decorated. We went into town and got some second-hand Degas prints for practically nothing. But best of all, borrowed a fabulous bullfight poster from her sister, who is not a student here, but guess what? The Registrar of the College! So Adele not only knows all the customs and traditions of this place, but all the rules and regulations as well. It's practically like living with a chaperone. Daddy, you couldn't have done better if you'd picked her out yourself."

(FRANK *is looking very pleased. The Michaelson living room goes off, and the dormitory comes on.* MOLLIE *and her roommate, a darling-looking girl named* ADELE MC-DOUGALL, *are surveying with satisfaction the results of their decorating, which runs to checked bedspreads and a large bullfight poster over one of the beds*)

ADELE   (*On her bed*)   I think we're a couple of damn geniuses. (*Hops up on the other bed and adjusts poster*) Maybe we ought to go in for interior decorating.

MOLLIE It's absolutely fabulous. Everything! (*Looks out window*) The campus is just beautiful. As a matter of fact, the only thing wrong with Hawthorne College for Women—is that there are no men.

ADELE (*Taps the side of her head sagely*) Now I can see why you got fifteen-o-four on the College Boards. Right to the heart of the matter.

MOLLIE Well, how do you get to meet some? Is there a system? I mean, do we sign up some place?

ADELE (*Comfortably*) Oh, they find you. They have the same needs you do. Right now, two gung-ho freshmen at Dartmouth are trying to figure out how to get down here and attack you and me.
(*At that moment,* SARAH WALKER *comes into their room.* SARAH *is about the same age as the other girls, but is much more sophisticated. She wears the same kind of clothes they do, but hers always look a little better. She is quite stunning. She carries a cigarette in a long holder*)

SARAH (*Near the doorway*) This place is a goddam *nunnery.* (*She takes a long drag at her cigarette and paces across the room*)

MOLLIE Oh, hello, Sarah. You talking about the same thing we are?

SARAH To whom? Did you see what I drew for a roommate? (*Turns her eyes up to heaven*) Quelle horreur, mes enfants! (*Puffs cigarette, turns her back to the audience; looks around the room at the prints and posters*) Your room looks like a dream. You know what the décor of our dump is? Gold

cups! She's got a gold cup for tennis, swimming, basketball.
I've got my toothbrush in a gold cup for Sportsmanship!
(*She sits on a bed*)

MOLLIE   Sarah, what are you doing in college, anyway?

SARAH   It's all my mother's idea. She's been married seven or
eight times, and every once in a while she gets a spasm that
I'm being neglected. My presence here is the result of one of
those spasms. Actually, parents are idiots. They don't know,
and I'm certainly not going to tell them, but kids whose parents are divorced get twice as much attention as the other
kind. (*Looks out the window and stands transfixed*) My
God! Men! (MOLLIE *and* ADELE *turn as one and stare out
window, both demanding to know "Where?"*) Getting out
of that car. (*Crosses to* ADELE) They're from Hah-vad.

MOLLIE   How can you tell?

SARAH   There's no sticker on the windshield. Imagine! They
drove all the way from Harvard! That blond one's cute.

MOLLIE   What are they doing here?

ADELE   They've come to look over the new crop.

MOLLIE   Us?

ADELE   Who else? They sort of prowl around and earmark
what they like for future reference. Shall we?
(*She opens the door*)

SARAH   Certainly. Coming, Mollie?

MOLLIE   It's perfectly revolting. (*Turns to look out the window; doesn't see* ADELE *and* SARAH *exit*) Do you girls really
plan to go parading out there to be looked over like prize

pigs at the Pomona Fair? Why, I would no more do anything like that than ... (*Turns and realizes* ADELE *and* SARAH *have gone*) Where is everybody?

(*Scrambles over the bed, looks down the hall. Then, she looks out the window again. After a moment, she smooths her hair and runs out after the other girls. The dormitory disappears, and at stage center the campus fence comes on. Three boys are leaning against it, surveying the passing scene. They are the blond, good-looking one named* DONN BOWDRY, *who is a junior and very wise; a small chunky freshman who will be called* 1ST FRESHMAN; *and a burly, athletic type who will be called* 2ND FRESHMAN)

DONN All in all, this is our best bet. It's close enough so you don't have to pay for hotel rooms on weekends, and they come in the same shapes and with the same accessories as you'll find at any other institution of learning.

1ST FRESHMAN How coöperative are they?

DONN Well, don't try to make it on the first date. The American female finds that insulting. On the other hand, I understand from some guy who was on a Fulbright last year that European women—

1ST FRESHMAN (*Sees imaginary girl. Gestures to* DONN) Hey, take a look at that.

DONN Hi! Glad to see you back. (*With their eyes, the boys appreciately follow her progress across the stage, left to right. When she has gone,* 1ST FRESHMAN *looks questioningly at* DONN. *He shakes his head*) Junior. Pinned. M.I.T. Madly in love. Sea-green incorruptible. Our game is freshmen.

(*They nod sagely to indicate their mature understanding*)

1ST FRESHMAN (*Pointing*) That one looks nice. The one in the checked pants.

DONN (*After a look*) My dear boy, she's an absolute pig.

1ST FRESHMAN Listen, I'm no beauty myself.

DONN (*Gazing raptly off*) Wow! Take a look.
(*The other two look also*)

2ND FRESHMAN Are they new?

DONN (*Without taking his eyes off the girls*) I never saw them before—and if I never see the tall one again, I'll kill myself.
(SARAH *and* ADELE *come on, left, and walk demurely past the boys. The boys watch with admiration as the girls go by, not hurrying their pace. As soon as they have gone by the boys,* SARAH *stops*)

SARAH (*Offering her pack*) Cigarette, *Adele?*

ADELE Thank you, *Sarah.*
(*Slowly,* SARAH *lights* ADELE's *cigarette and her own.* MOLLIE *comes rushing on from left; as soon as she sees the boys, she slows down, and joins her friends*)

SARAH No need to rush, *Mollie.* I'm just going to post a letter.
(SARAH *and* ADELE *proceed off right.* MOLLIE *takes a backward look at the boys, and follows. The boys watch their every movement*)

2ND FRESHMAN Well? What do we do now? Just stand here?

DONN (*Nods calmly*) Mmmhmmm. You heard her. She's just going to post a letter. There's no mailbox down there—and there *is* one right in the dorm. (*Very sure of himself*) They'll be back.

(*Two other boys enter. They are upperclassmen, typical collegiate types named* RICHARD GLUCK *and* ALFRED GREIFFINGER)

RICHARD Hey, Harvard, anything good around?

DONN Dogs, nothing but dogs. (*Elaborately*) So dismal we're contemplating doing our military service this year.

1ST FRESHMAN Yeah. As soon as we get back to town, we're enlisting.

RICHARD (*Catches on quickly*) Oh. Found something good, huh?

DONN Yeah. But let's not spoil it with a snow job, shall we? (RICHARD *looks offstage right. The girls are evidently returning and he reacts with proper reverence*)

RICHARD Ma-ma mia! (*The girls are near enough to be recognized*) Hey! That's Mollie Michaelson! (MOLLIE, ADELE *and* SARAH *enter. All excited*) Went to high school with me. Two years behind me. Boy, she's grown up! Mollie!

MOLLIE (*Peers at him a moment*) Richard! Richard Gluck! (*Runs; they embrace like old friends*) Somebody told me you were at M.I.T. (*They break away and smile at each other*) Oh, girls, I want you to meet Richard Gluck. (SARAH *and* ADELE *join* MOLLIE) Richard, this is my roommate, Adele McDougall, and another friend of mine, Sarah Walker.

27

(*They exchange how-do-you-do's as all the boys make mental notes of the names*)

RICHARD And this is a classmate of mine, Alfred Greiffinger. (*Another exchange of greetings.* DONN *and his chums line up, ready to be presented.* RICHARD *turns his back on them pointedly*)

SARAH (*In a half-whisper*) Mollie . . . (*Indicates the other boys; she has had her eye on* DONN)

MOLLIE (*Nods*) Richard, who are they?

RICHARD I don't know. Think they run a kennel in town, or something. Come on, let's all go have some coffee. (*Links arms with* MOLLIE *and starts off left*) All freshmen?
(SARAH *follows with* ADELE *and* GREIFFINGER)

SARAH Mmmmhmmm. Untouched by human hands.
(*They are out, leaving* DONN *and his two despondent friends behind*)

1ST FRESHMAN Well? I thought you were going to kill yourself?

DONN Not me. Sarah Walker, Mollie Michaelson, and Adele . . .

2ND FRESHMAN (*Supplies the name, wistfully*) McDougall.

DONN (*Nods*) There's a lot of time ahead of us, a long, cold winter, and the time of the singing of birds will come.
(*The campus fence and the boys have gone off through that, and action starts again in the Michaelson living room, where* FRANK *is finishing the letter, as* ANNE *and* LIZ *listen*)

FRANK "So Friday night I went out with Richard Gluck, and Saturday night I went out with a fraternity brother of his who is a junior named Alfred Greiffinger, who took me to dinner and a lecture by Margaret Mead, who said that young people at college should not marry but should experiment."

(*He looks at* ANNE)

ANNE Who said that? Margaret Mead or Greiffinger?

FRANK (*Studies letter*) Apparently Margaret Mead, because . . . (*Continues to read*) "I was under the impression that she meant experiment mentally, but later on I found out he thought physically, and since we reacted so differently, I don't think I'll be seeing much of Alfred Greiffinger any more. (*A sigh of relief*) Anyway, this Friday it's Richard Gluck again, and Saturday Adele has dated me with a Williams boy from her home town who she says is utterly obnoxious. (*A pause*) But *anything* is better than being without a date on Saturday night. I know this probably sounds awful to you, but that is an accepted fact in this female society of which I have now become a member, and I haven't been here long enough to start being a nonconformist, nor have I any desire to. I have signed up for English, French, Biology and Modern European History. Two of my instructors are crocks—(LIZ *laughs.* FRANK *evidently doesn't see anything amusing*) but my History professor is fabulous. Oh, by the way, we've put in our own telephone, Maple 6-2984. (ANNE *writes the number down on a pad*) Love, Mollie." There's a P.S. (*He follows Mollie's handwriting up the side of the page*) She doesn't want to wear her retainer. And P.P.S. (*Reads slowly, deciphering the writing*) "I heard Norman Thomas speak last Monday night on disarmament, which he naturally regards as absolutely necessary, and isn't the world situation just abysmal? Sometimes I think it won't last another week—and . . . here I am . . . still a . . . "

(FRANK's *voice trails off. A thoroughly disillusioned man, he puts the letter down, folds it over and hands it to* ANNE. ANNE *rereads the letter from the beginning, with relish*)

ANNE I think it's marvelous. Or should I say fabulous?

FRANK What's fabulous about it? They're handing her around like a hot potato.

ANNE This is the time for her to be handed around. And Mollie can take care of herself. You saw the way she managed that Greiffinger person. She won't get into trouble.

FRANK (*Gets up*) I didn't send her three thousand miles just not to get into trouble! (*Strides toward the telephone*) I'm going to call her.

ANNE (*Blocks him off*) No, Frank, no! Don't call her when you're angry. Wait till tonight when you've cooled off and the rates are down. (FRANK *sits*) Come on. (ANNE *tries to pull* FRANK *to his feet*) Let's practice your rhumba.

FRANK (*Refuses to get up*) No, Annie, no. Anyway, I can only do it with a chair on my head. I can see myself for years at parties—every time they put on a rhumba, I pick up a chair! Pretty soon people will stop inviting us. We'll sit here alone, night after night. We'll take to drink. All because you said we ought to go to Arthur Murray's! That was a terrible thing to do, Annie.

(*The Michaelson living room disappears. The dormitory room now appears.* MOLLIE *and* ADELE *are studying.*

MOLLIE *is on the bed, reading from a thick literary
tome.* ADELE *is sketching a diagram with great concen-
tration. Both girls are in pajamas and robes*)

MOLLIE (*Reading*)
"When in disgrace with Fortune and men's eyes,
I all alone beweep my outcast state,
And trouble deaf heaven with my bootless cries,
And look upon myself, and curse my fate,
Wishing me like ..."

ADELE Mollie, please. I'm diagraming the inside of a frog, and
I put her pancreas where her stomach ought to be.
(*Sighs and starts to erase.* MOLLIE *reads a little more to
herself and exhales ecstatically*)

MOLLIE How could I have got to be eighteen years old and
not realize how fabulous Shakespeare's sonnets are? (*The
phone rings.* MOLLIE *picks it up from floor.* ADELE *also reaches,
but too late*) Hello? ... (*Enthusiastically*) Why, hello, Alfred!

ADELE Who?
(*She looks at her questioningly.* MOLLIE *covers the
mouthpiece and hisses*)

MOLLIE Greiffinger! (*Back to the phone, sweetly*) Oh, I'm
so sorry. I already have a date for next Saturday. Can I
have a rain check? ... Good ... (*Rises and crosses with
the phone to the desk*) I'll look forward to hearing from
you.
(*She hangs up, puts the phone on the desk*)

ADELE Who you going with next Saturday?

MOLLIE (*Flops on her stomach on her bed*) Nobody. (*Back to Shakespeare*)
"Let me not to the marriage of true minds
Admit impediments. Love is not love
Which alters when it alteration finds . . . "
(*Puts book down and looks at* ADELE, *seriously*) Do you suppose this is all a waste? I mean, let's face it, woman's real purpose in life is marriage, children, propagate the species, and all that stuff. Does it make you any more desirable as a wife because you know the meaning of a Shakespeare sonnet, or you can describe intimately the inner workings of a female frog?

ADELE   I intend to keep it a secret. Might scare somebody away. How many articles have you read on the aggressive American female?

MOLLIE   Exactly. But if they teach us all this stuff, aren't we supposed to use it? And if we use it, does that make us aggressive?
(SARAH, *also in robe and pajamas, enters and yells back into corridor*)

SARAH   Well, if you don't like it, go to the goddam house mother and tell her I smoke cigars and you want a new roommate. (SARAH *slams door and sits on edge of* ADELE'S *bed. Now utterly charming to* MOLLIE *and* ADELE) Listen, *mes amies,* I have a weekend date at Yale, and he has a friend. (*Looks from one to the other*) Now, who's available? Before you snap at this golden opportunity, I want to warn you—he's short.

ADELE   I have no problem . . . I'm planning to defend my honor in Dartmouth this weekend.

SARAH Dartmouth? (*Shrugs*) Many have tried—few have succeeded. (*To* MOLLIE) Anyway, that narrows the field considerably.

MOLLIE (*Warily*) How short is he?

SARAH Five-two. (*Hastily*) But what the hell? It's a chance to see Yale, we'd be together, and who knows what you might meet down there.

MOLLIE Yeah, but ...

SARAH Come on, Mollie. Listen, my mother's happiest marriage was the shortest . . . in height, I mean.

MOLLIE Okay. But this is a weekend date. I'll need a letter of permission. There isn't time to write ...

SARAH Why don't you wire?

MOLLIE Yes. I could do that. What's his name?

SARAH (*Rises*) Stanley Underdown. (MOLLIE *and* ADELE *stare at her*) I can't help it.

MOLLIE And short, too. They're always the hardest to handle. Always trying to *prove* something.
(*The phone rings*—ADELE *picks it up*)

ADELE Hello? Yes, she's here. Mollie, long distance.
(MOLLIE *scrambles over her bed and grabs the phone. The Michaelson living room comes to life.* FRANK *is on the phone, with* ANNE *hovering to get the sound of* MOLLIE'S *voice*)

MOLLIE Hello!

FRANK (*His anger evaporates like magic. He is beaming*)
Hello, Mollie. How are you, sweetie?

MOLLIE I'm just fine, Daddy. Wonderful to talk to you. How are you and Mom and Liz?

FRANK Fine. I'm glad I found you in. How's college?

MOLLIE Just wonderful.

FRANK What are you doing?

MOLLIE I'm right in the middle of a paper on the sonnets of Shakespeare. Isn't Shakespeare fabulous, Daddy?

FRANK (*To* ANNE) Shakespeare is fabulous, too.

MOLLIE What?

FRANK Nothing, darling.

MOLLIE Is there something wrong, Daddy?

FRANK No, no.

MOLLIE You're sure everything's all right?

FRANK Yes, yes. I just wanted to talk to you . . .

MOLLIE (*Sits on bed*) Well, it's marvelous that you did, because I have this wonderful invitation to go to New Haven for the weekend, but I need your permission. So will you please write a letter to my house mother, her name is Miss Helen Pickett, with two "t's," and say that it's all right for me to spend the weekend at Yale as the guest of Stanley Underdown?

FRANK Who? Do I know him?

MOLLIE Of course not. I don't even know him myself. I'm being fixed up.

FRANK (*Appalled*) You're being what?
(SARAH *crosses to* MOLLIE)

SARAH He lives in the same house that Averell Harriman lived in.

MOLLIE He lives in the same house as Averell Harriman.

FRANK Averell Harriman! Are you going out with him?

MOLLIE Of course not.

ANNE (*All excited*) What about Averell Harriman.

FRANK I don't understand a damn word of this.

MOLLIE Never mind. Just write it. You also have to say you understand that suitable housing will be arranged and you absolve Hawthorne College of all responsibility for me on the weekend. Daddy, will you please get that in the mail tonight?

FRANK I'll do nothing of the kind!
(MOLLIE *rises, paces*)

ANNE What? What?

FRANK She wants to spend the weekend at Yale, suitably housed with some unknown character named Stanley Underdown!

ANNE How perfectly marvelous. Give me that. (*Takes phone*) Mollie, dear, it's Mom. Now tell me exactly what I have to do.
(*She takes notes*)

MOLLIE (*Sits on bed*) Hi, Mom! Wonderful to talk to you. Now, all you have to do is write a letter to my house mother, Miss Helen Pickett, with two "t's" ...

ANNE (*Noting the name*) Yes, dear. What else?

MOLLIE And say that I have your permission to go to Yale ...

ANNE Yale! How wonderful, darling!

MOLLIE ... as the guest of Stanley Underdown, spell it just the way it sounds ...

ANNE (*Busily writing*) It sounds dreadful, dear, but I will ... (*As* MOLLIE *signals an "okay" to* SARAH, *both Michaelson living room and dormitory disappear, and the stage now represents the street outside the Michaelson home. There is a mailbox at the extreme left.* EMMETT *is at stage center, listening to chamber music on a small transistor, which he holds to his ear, and gazing up at* MOLLIE'S *window. After a moment,* FRANK *appears, a letter in his hand. There is a bemused expression on his face. He walks right past* EMMETT *without seeing him, on his way to mailbox*)

EMMETT Hello, Mr. Michaelson.

FRANK Hello ... (*Peers at him in the darkness*) Who's that? Oh, Arnold!

EMMETT It's Emmett, Mr. Michaelson.

FRANK (*Suddenly* EMMETT *looks good to him*) Oh, Emmett! Emmett, I'm so glad to see you.
(*They shake hands*)

EMMETT How's Mollie? Have you heard from her?

FRANK   Yes. As a matter of fact, I just talked to her on the phone a little while ago.

EMMETT   I don't suppose she mentioned me?

FRANK   (*Carefully*)   Well, she asked how everybody was, so I suppose you could . . .

EMMETT   (*Dolefully*)   Mmm-hmmm.

FRANK   (*With a keen look at him*)   Having a bad time?

EMMETT   Well . . . (*Turns front; quotes, philosophically*) "Men have died . . . and worms have eaten them, but not for love." I'll survive. I suppose you'll think it's stupid, but you know what I'm doing here? (*Looks down*) Every once in a while I just come over and stand across the street and look up at her window.

FRANK   My boy, forget her. You've lost her, I've lost her, we've both lost her. (*Brandishes the letter*) Shall I tell you what's in this letter? Permission for her to spend the weekend at Yale with a total stranger!

EMMETT   (*Bristling with outrage*)   Well, do you think that's right?

FRANK   I don't. I most certainly do not. I fought against it like a tiger. But she's got permission and I signed it.

EMMETT   (*After a moment's thought*)   Mr. Michaelson, why don't you let me mail the letter for you?

FRANK   Oh, no. I thought of that. I have to live with these people—(*Starts off; sighs heavily*) Fathers of sons have a much easier time of it.

EMMETT Mr. Michaelson, I'm going to tell you something. You've got nothing to worry about with Mollie. (*Crosses to* FRANK) Why, I once spent three hours on the top of Mulholland Drive trying to talk her into . . . (*Breaks off, confused*) Well, what I mean is . . .

FRANK (*Wrathfully, as he backs* EMMETT *across the stage*) I know exactly what you mean! (*Then, philosophically*) Well . . . East, West . . . I can see that geography has nothing to do with it. I might as well put this in the mail. Good night, Arnold.

EMMETT (*Starts to correct him, decides it's not worth while*) Good night, Mr. Michaelson.
(*They go in opposite directions.* FRANK *drops letter into mailbox, then comes down to proscenium, stage left, and talks to the audience*)

FRANK I don't know why I took it so big, because hot on the heels of Stanley Underdown came Adam Bassington, from Dartmouth; Leland Mendez, Princeton; Darcy MacNamara, Holy Cross; Johann Sebastian Vogel, Brandeis—and they all got permission to spend the weekend with Mollie and Hawthorne College was absolved of all responsibility. And then one day we got a letter saying, "He doesn't know it yet, but I have met a boy from Harvard who's going to marry me." That's all. That one didn't even have a name.
(*The lights dim on* FRANK *as he exits. Lights come up stage right to show* MOLLIE *dancing with* DONN BOWDRY. ADELE *is seated at a restaurant table with a most intellectual and argumentative young man named* ALEX LOOMIS. *They appear to be not speaking. Both work on the lobsters on the table before them and watch the dancing. Dim music is heard*)

MOLLIE Well, I'm having a marvelous time, but I think we ought to go back to the table.

DONN Oh? Why?

MOLLIE He's my date and there's no reason why Adele should be stuck with him.
> (DONN *shrugs, and they go back to the table.* ALEX *makes a half-hearted attempt to rise, then slumps back as* MOLLIE *is seated*)

DONN Adele? Dance?

ADELE Love to.
> (*They go to dance floor.* MOLLIE *starts on her lobster. She exchanges a frosty smile with* ALEX *and watches the dancing wistfully*)

ALEX It never fails.

MOLLIE (*Coming to with a start*) What?

ALEX I said it never fails. Every time I double with Donn, my so-called date spends the entire evening admiring him.

MOLLIE I wasn't admiring him. I was looking at him and Adele dancing. Is there anything wrong with that?

ALEX No. Go ahead. Watch them dance.

MOLLIE I'm sorry, Alex. We could talk, if you like.

ALEX It's risky, but I'm perfectly willing. What shall we talk about? How about One World?

MOLLIE (*With a deep breath*) All right, Alex. Do you believe in One World?

ALEX Do you?

MOLLIE Yes. Do you?

ALEX No, I don't.

MOLLIE Why not?

ALEX When something comes along that everybody believes in, you have to examine it very carefully.

MOLLIE Then you're against it.

ALEX Oh, I'm not against everybody having a place in the sun. There's no stopping that. But the corollary notion that all people are equal is obviously ridiculous. (*Expanding*) There will always be people of superior intelligence. In every tribal group, some people are born smarter than other people. There's no point to providing equal opportunity for everybody. Those who are better equipped should have better opportunity.
   (*A pause for breath*)

MOLLIE I see. What speech would you have made if I'd said I didn't believe in One World?

ALEX (*Looks at* MOLLIE *keenly*) That's very astute of you. I didn't think you were that bright.

MOLLIE (*Miffed*) I'm not. A dull-normal could tell that about you. (*Digs into her lobster, determined to enjoy something*) This lobster is delicious. How's yours?

ALEX All right. (*Unable to agree about anything*) But if you'd ever had lobster on a beach in Maine, cooked over hot rocks and covered with seaweed . . .

MOLLIE Well, I haven't! I'm from Southern California and this tastes great!

ALEX Tell me, is Southern California really the intellectual desert everybody says it is?

MOLLIE (*Restrains herself a moment, then*) Certainly. Why, before I came East, I thought Marcel Prowst (*purposely mispronounced*) was some kind of new hairdo.

ALEX Oh . . . (*He's very young*) By the way, it's Proust.

MOLLIE Really? You learn something new here every day, don't you? It's so stimulating.
    (ADELE *and* DONN *return*)

ADELE But she looks perfectly miserable; she looks as if she's going to break a plate over his head any minute.

DONN It has happened. A Vassar girl.

ADELE A Vassar girl? They're so isolated I'd thought they'd stand for anything. (*Indicates she'd like him to dance with* MOLLIE) I'll go powder my nose.
    (*He nods.* ADELE *goes and* DONN *goes to the table where* MOLLIE *and* ALEX *are eating in dogged silence*)

DONN Mollie . . . would you like to . . . ?
    (*Indicates dance floor*)

MOLLIE (*Half out of her seat*) Would I! (*Remembers her manners*) You don't mind, do you, Alex?

ALEX But you're right in the middle of your lobster. Aren't you going to finish it?

MOLLIE No, no. I've had enough.

ALEX Maybe I should get the waiter to keep it hot for you . . .

MOLLIE (*Going off with* DONN) Don't bother with the waiter.
You just *talk* to it!
(DONN *takes her in his arms and they dance off together.*
ALEX *settles back in his place, very disgruntled*)

DONN Sorry if you're not having a very good time.

MOLLIE Oh, that's all right. Is your friend on the debating
team?

DONN Organized activity? Alex? He might take on the whole
team, he'd never join it.

MOLLIE I've had some tough dates, but he and I are the mis-
match of the century.

DONN You know something, Mollie? I think so, too. We can't
do anything about it tonight, but you and I are a much more
interesting combination.
(ADELE *re-enters.* ALEX *doesn't see her. She holds the
back of her chair, lifts it, thumps it smartly on the floor
and sits.* ALEX *stands up belatedly, knocks his chair over*)

ALEX (*Picking up his chair*) Terribly sorry. I'm not used to
being out in civilized society.

ADELE Perfectly all right.

ALEX (*Directly*) I don't suppose you want to dance, do you?

ADELE How can I resist such a charming invitation?
(*They go out onto dance floor.* ALEX *takes her in
his arms, and they dance together, perfectly smoothly,
gracefully.* ADELE *looks up at him in surprise.* MOLLIE,
dancing with DONN, *turns in time to catch* ALEX's *per-*

formance and also registers surprise. ALEX *goes into a deep dip with* ADELE, *and they dance off right*)

MOLLIE That is the most unpredictable human being I have ever met in my whole life!

DONN Forget him. Look, Mollie, I don't usually work this fast, but we might not be alone together the rest of the time. So, what are you doing next Saturday?

MOLLIE (*Pulls away*) I don't know.

DONN Of course you do. Now what about the Saturday after that?

MOLLIE Am I being snowed?

DONN I wouldn't use a line on you. That's so dull. I just want to see you Saturday, and the Saturday after that, and the Saturday after that . . .

MOLLIE That's a pretty good line. But I like it.
      (*She and* DONN *dance off left, as restaurant set disappears. The Michaelson living room rolls on from right. At the left end of the couch, a small easel has been set up, holding a canvas with its back to audience.* FRANK *is on the opposite end of the couch, holding palette and brushes, as he lines up with his thumb the effect he wants to achieve on the canvas. He gets up and starts to paint, with great concentration, what appears to be a series of straight lines.* ANNE *comes in, carrying some sewing, and looks pleased to see him at work*)

ANNE Wouldn't it be extraordinary if you turned out to have talent?

43

FRANK (*Painting*) Not particularly.

ANNE (*Looks at the painting*) What are you . . . doing this time?

FRANK I'm painting us a Mondrian.

ANNE Oh!

FRANK Got my inspiration from the linoleum in the kitchen. (*He stops in the middle of a bold stroke*) Isn't it about time we heard from Mollie?

ANNE (*Crosses and sits on sofa*) How often did you write home when you were at college? Mollie's in love. She's happy.

FRANK Donn! Donn! Donn! What do we know about this boy, actually?

ANNE Well, Mollie wrote about his family. They're wealthy, they live in New York . . .

FRANK And they spend most of their time traveling in Europe! I don't like that.

ANNE (*Astonished*) What do you mean, you don't like that? What's wrong with traveling in Europe?

FRANK He just doesn't sound right for Mollie. Sounds like everything's being handed to him on a gold plate.

ANNE Oh, I know what you want. You want a boy who comes from Scranton, Pennsylvania, and they dragged him up out of a mine, gave him a scholarship, and shipped him off to Harvard!

FRANK (*In complete accord*) Yeah. Why doesn't Mollie find someone like that?

ANNE You're going to discriminate against people just because they're wealthy? What kind of snob are you?

FRANK (*Trying a new tack*) Well, anyway, isn't Mollie a little young to have decided on one boy? I mean you went with lots of boys before I came along. You shopped around a little.

ANNE Frank, last month you were complaining bitterly because she was dating too many boys. You said she was being handed around like a hot potato. You didn't like that.

FRANK (*Firmly*) No, I didn't.

ANNE Don't you like it better now that she's only dating Donn?

FRANK (*Just as firmly*) No, I don't.

ANNE I give up. (*She starts off.* FRANK *tosses his palette angrily on the couch, takes up a large yardstick, holds it against the canvas—it extends over the top by a foot and a half—and paints a straight line, using the stick as a guide.* ANNE *watches as he turns the yardstick and paints another line at a right angle to it*) Oh, I think that's cheating.

FRANK (*Imperturbably*) Mondrian has his methods, I have mine.

> (*Lights go out in Michaelson living room and a dim light comes on at extreme left, to show a campus bench.* ALEX *and* SARAH *are seated on the bench, in close embrace. Their dialogue consists chiefly of "Yes" from* ALEX, *and "No" from* SARAH. ALEX *moves in even closer and*

tries to hook his leg around her. She pushes him away suddenly)

SARAH   Stop it, Alex, stop it!

ALEX   Ah, come on.
(*He lunges. They struggle for a moment)*

SARAH   For heaven's sake, take it easy. You'll knock out my contact lenses!

ALEX (*Lets go suddenly and turns away)* Oh, God! (SARAH *searches in her purse for her compact)* Have you ever used that line before?

SARAH (*Complacently)* Mmmhmmm. (*Finds comb, lipstick and compact)* It sure knocks the hell out of romance, doesn't it?

ALEX   Who says it has to be romantic?

SARAH   Well, I'm just as avant-garde as the next one, but there must be some pretense. You can't even *pretend* your heart is in it. (*Looks at herself in the mirror and starts to repair the damage)* You know, Alex, you're really quite sweet.

ALEX   What a bitchy thing to say.

SARAH   Oh, no. You are, and I intend to tell Mollie I found you fascinating.

ALEX   Resistible, but fascinating.

SARAH   Oh, practically everybody's resistible.

ALEX   Aaaah ... I've given up on Mollie. She's being snowed by the champ. Donn is a kind of male Marilyn Monroe.

Elizabeth Ashley, Art Carney, and Louise Sorrell as MOLLIE
MICHAELSON, FRANK MICHAELSON, and SARAH WALKER

Elizabeth Ashley, Art Carney, and Louise Sorrell as MOLLIE
MICHAELSON, FRANK MICHAELSON, and SARAH WALKER

SARAH   He's quite the operator. Have you seen Mollie lately? (*She puts the things back in her purse*)

ALEX   No.

SARAH   Mmmm—*Très élégante, mon ami*—I think she and Donn . . .

ALEX   I don't want to hear about them. The hell with sex. I'm giving it up for the New Year.

SARAH   And it isn't even Christmas yet. (*Rests her head on his shoulder*) *Joyeux Noël,* Alex.

ALEX (*Elegantly*)   Ap-cray!

SARAH   Well, it's been a delightful evening. (*She gets up.* ALEX *doesn't move, gazes gloomily ahead*) Don't bother seeing me to my door.
(*She goes.* ALEX *sits a moment in silence*)

ALEX   Oh, hell!
(*Lights go out on the bench. Then the street outside the Michaelson home appears. It is night. After a moment,* FRANK *walks on from the direction of the house. It is winter, and he wears a heavy carcoat*)

FRANK   Well, today is the day. (*Grins amiably*) Mollie's coming home. Just called the airport. The plane's only forty-five minutes late. (*Sighs with anticipation*) This is the longest she's ever been away from us . . . (*Ticks off on his fingers*) September, October, November, December . . . And I still can't do the rhumba . . . I wonder if *she* learned anything. (*Shrugs*) I don't really care. I just want to see her.
(ANNE *comes out to join him, followed by* LIZ. *Both wear coats*)

ANNE Frank, I called the airport again. The plane's on time.

FRANK It is? (*Consults his watch*) Those damn airlines. Do they know what they're doing?
(*He brushes past them, and out*)

LIZ Mother, I think you'd better drive!
(ANNE *nods and they follow. There is the sound of a jet engine screaming in for a landing. This becomes the sound of the car engine. A door slams. During all this, the Michaelson living room has rolled on. No one is on the stage, but the lamps are lit and the Chistmas season is evidenced by a Christmas mobile in a corner of the room and various gift-wrapped parcels.* LIZ's *voice can be heard babbling away offstage right*)

LIZ (*Indistinctly*) Be careful getting out of the car . . . And the football team is an absolute disaster this year. After five games they finally scored a touchdown, and there was so much cheering it was positively humiliating. Of course, football isn't important, but still . . .
(*In course of this,* ANNE *comes in first, looking distraught. She takes off her coat, drops it on a chair, and turns toward the door.* FRANK *follows her in. He is stunned. He carries* MOLLIE's *large bag, walks with it to the far end of the couch, drops it on floor, and also turns toward door.* LIZ *now comes in, also carrying some of* MOLLIE's *possessions*)

LIZ Everyone is dying to see you. The phone's been ringing all day.
(MOLLIE *comes in and takes a long look around at the room. The cause for shock is quite apparent. She is wearing a sophisticated black coat and dress; long ear-*

*rings dangle just above her shoulders; her hair is ar-
ranged in a bubble cut; she puffs inexpertly at a
cigarette in a long holder. The family studies her*)

MOLLIE (*Finally*) I've been thinking about this moment for
weeks. (*Another pause to look around.* ANNE *comes downstage for a closer look at her. She still doesn't believe it*) It
seems so much smaller. Have you done something to it?

ANNE Oh, no, dear, I don't think so.

MOLLIE Everybody says there's nothing very Christmasy about
Southern California—but I *feel* very Christmasy. (*Drags on
her cigarette as she turns to face her father.* FRANK *sits suddenly on sofa.* MOLLIE *notices the sunken look on his face and
goes to him*) What's the matter, Daddy?

FRANK I don't know. Except maybe—just to keep pace—I
should have raised a little beard while you were gone.
    (MOLLIE *laughs*)

ANNE Darling, did you have a good sleep on the plane?

MOLLIE (*Crosses to* ANNE) No. As a matter of fact, I didn't
sleep at all.

ANNE Oh ... but I thought ... your hair ...

MOLLIE (*Bristling slightly*) What about my hair?

ANNE Well, nothing, nothing. I just didn't realize you do it
that way deliberately.

MOLLIE I *knew* you wouldn't like it. (*Appeals to* FRANK) Do
you, Daddy?

FRANK I'm not sure. I have to get used to it first.

49

MOLLIE *Donn* is crazy about it.

LIZ I like it. I wonder how it would look on me ...

ANNE Shut up.

MOLLIE Well, now that the initial shock of seeing me is over
—may I have a martini, please? Very dry?
(FRANK *just stares at her a moment*)

FRANK No! (*Gets up*) Not even very wet!

MOLLIE (*Crosses to* FRANK) Daddy, that's perfectly ridiculous.
I drink on dates. What do you want me to do? Smoke behind the fence?

FRANK (*A helpless look at* ANNE. *She shrugs*) Oh, all right.
(*He starts toward the drink setup*)

MOLLIE What kind of gin do you use?

FRANK (*Pauses for a moment for control*) My own label!
I've been making it in the cellar for years!
(ANNE *takes* FRANK's *coat and he starts to mix drinks*)

MOLLIE Donn says House of Lords is the only gin.

FRANK Really? And what vermouth?

MOLLIE Noilly Prat, of course.

FRANK (*Stirs drinks*) Outside of a bartender, what's Donn
studying to be?

MOLLIE Oh, Daddy, they *all* have to go into the Service first.
But after that, he's planning to be an international tycoon,
or some such.

50

ANNE   Some such?

MOLLIE   They *all* want to make money.

FRANK   (*Pouring a drink*)   Well, there's nothing wrong with that.
   (*He hands* MOLLIE *her drink*)

MOLLIE   (*Holds her drink. Everybody watches to see what she'll do with it*)   Isn't anybody going to drink with me?

FRANK   Certainly.
   (*He holds the martini pitcher to his mouth*)

ANNE   Frank!

FRANK   Oh, all right. (*He pours for himself and* ANNE; *addresses* LIZ *with mock politeness*) What about you, Liz?
   (*He gestures invitingly with glass and pitcher*)

LIZ   (*Grandly*)   Since you haven't got House of Lords, I'm not interested.

FRANK   (*Sits on the hassock with his drink*)   Well, what's college like, Mollie? Is it all it's cracked up to be?

MOLLIE   (*Crosses to* FRANK)   I'm on cloud seven, Daddy. I can't wait to get back.

FRANK   (*Miffed*)   Thanks.

MOLLIE   (*Kneels beside him*)   Oh, I don't mean it that way. Of course I love all of you . . . (*Stands up*) But aside from that—what is there for me here? I've outgrown all my friends.

FRANK   They didn't just stand still. They got older, too.

MOLLIE (*Patiently*) Daddy, there's just something about the *East*. It's ... well, it's the *East*.

FRANK I'll go along with that.

MOLLIE (*Sits on the couch, puts her drink down*) Do you know that out of sixteen Rhodes scholars chosen from all over the United States—seven came from Harvard?

ANNE (*Sits on the hassock beside* FRANK) I think that's very interesting, don't you, Frank?

FRANK No. Not particularly. I wasn't asking about Harvard. I was asking about Hawthorne College for Women.

MOLLIE Don't you see? It's all part of the same intellectual climate.

FRANK Oh. Are you planning to be the first woman Rhodes scholar?

MOLLIE Not a chance. Not me. I'm just about skinning through.

FRANK (*Gets up, crosses to* MOLLIE, *shocked*) You're kidding!

MOLLIE (*Quite calmly*) I am not. You might just as well make up your mind to it. (*Rattles off her words quickly; this has all been thought out long ago*) The only way you can get honors at Hawthorne is by being an absolute grind. You've got to work all the time and turn down dates. And if you do, people look at you as if you're absolutely queer or something. It's really an awful rat race. If you *don't* go out every weekend, you feel rejected; and if you *do* go out, you have this terrible sense of guilt ... After all, is that what you came to college for? The girls and I talked it all over. (*Philo-*

sophically) The only solution is to fall in love and have all the pressures removed.
    (*They all stare at her for a moment*)

FRANK (*Finally*) How?

MOLLIE It's very simple. That way you know exactly what you're doing every weekend, so you don't spend any time thinking about it.

FRANK (*Sits on the hassock*) Oh!

MOLLIE (*Gets up*) Well, I guess I ought to unpack.

ANNE (*A little fuddled*) Yes. If you're staying.
    (MOLLIE *looks at* ANNE, *then starts to pick up the big bag*)

FRANK I'll take that up for you, dear.
    (*He takes the bag and goes upstairs*)

MOLLIE Thanks, Daddy. (*She and* LIZ *gather up the rest of her possessions and start upstairs after* FRANK. *To* LIZ, *as they go*) How are things at good old Beverly High?

LIZ About the same. Joan Shockworth had to leave school.

MOLLIE No!

LIZ Well, you don't put on ten pounds in two months just by overeating ...
    (ANNE *is alone. She contemplates her martini seriously, puts her hand to her forehead. After a moment,* FRANK *returns*)

FRANK Now don't worry about it, Annie. It's just a stage.

ANNE I'm not worried.

FRANK Well, don't. She'll get over it. (*Reassuring himself*) It's . . . it's Hegelian. (*Paces*) Thesis, antithesis, synthesis. She'll be better off as a result.
  (*He sits beside* ANNE)

ANNE Well, I don't know how Hegel got into it, but I wish you wouldn't take it so seriously. It's really kind of funny. You send off what you think is going to be the first woman President of the United States—and you get back Betty Boop!

FRANK (*Gets up and crosses room*) Yes. You're absolutely right. It's not life or death. It's just a passing phase.

ANNE Exactly. Take a look at that martini. She didn't have more than a sip.

FRANK That's true. (*He drinks it*) Helps to take the pressure off. (*There is the sound of a car door slamming from outside.* FRANK *looks out the window*) Somebody in this house is getting flowers.

ANNE What?

FRANK There's a florist's truck just out . . . (*The doorbell rings.* ANNE *rises, puts her glass down on table*) I'll get it.
  (*He throws the door open to reveal* EMMETT, *who carries an extraordinary basket of flowers in which roses rub shoulders companionably with chrysanthemums and carnations, and daisies. The colors are not very compatible*)

EMMETT Good evening, Mr. Michaelson. (*He comes in, sets the flowers on the floor in front of the couch*)

FRANK Well, for heaven's sake, it's . . . er . . .
  (*He looks to* ANNE *for help*)

TAKE HER, SHE'S MINE

ANNE Emmett.

EMMETT (*Removing cap*) Good evening, Mrs. Michaelson.

ANNE How nice to see you, Emmett.

FRANK What *are* you?

EMMETT Christmas job. I need every cent I can lay my hands on this Christmas. Is Mollie home?

FRANK She's here. (*Calling.* EMMETT *puts his hat on the couch*) Mollie! Mollie!

MOLLIE'S VOICE Yes, Daddy?

FRANK (*Yelling back*) Emmett's here!

MOLLIE'S VOICE Hi, Emmett! I'll be right down.

EMMETT Hi, Mollie!

FRANK Annie, why don't we drive out to Santa Monica and pick out a Christmas tree?

ANNE Sounds exciting.

FRANK This year let's get a white tree with gold balls.

ANNE (*Horrified*) What on earth for?

FRANK Oh, I don't know. It's just so *West*.
(EMMETT *picks up a book*)

ANNE (*Laughs*) All right. Just let me check and see if we need anything else in town.
(*She goes*)

55

EMMETT I see you're reading *The Rise and Fall of the Third Reich*.

FRANK Mmm-hmmm.

EMMETT (*A considered opinion*) I found it—quite superficial.

FRANK You did?

EMMETT I think perhaps that's because we're too close to that event to be able to evaluate it properly. Don't you think so, sir?

FRANK Errr . . . (FRANK *is saved by* MOLLIE's *appearance*) Aaah! Here's Mollie.

EMMETT (*Puts book down*) Hello, Mollie.

MOLLIE (*Extends hand; quite grandly*) Emmett . . .
      (FRANK *sits on the hassock*)

EMMETT Here, (*He moves the flower basket in front of Mollie*) For you.

MOLLIE Oh, they're lovely, Emmett. But you shouldn't have spent so much . . .

EMMETT What's the difference? It's the sentiment, isn't it?
      (FRANK *makes a great show of not listening*)

MOLLIE Yes. But they look so expensive.

EMMETT (*Candidly*) Oh. They weren't expensive at all. I'm working for a florist this Christmas—and I took one flower out of each bunch.

MOLLIE (*A little cool*) I see.

EMMETT How are you, Mollie? Gee, I have a million things to say to you. (MOLLIE *nods*) What about riding around Bel-Air on the truck with me, while I make my deliveries?

MOLLIE I'd love to, Emmett, but I just got off the plane and I didn't have five minutes' sleep last night . . .
(*She sits on the couch*)

EMMETT (*Sits beside her*) You look just fine to me, Mollie. (*Heartily. Points to hair*) Just comb your hair and come on. (FRANK *looks pained for* EMMETT)

MOLLIE (*Ice-cold now*) What?

EMMETT (*Nothing gets through to him*) Then just come on. Nobody's going to see you anyway.

MOLLIE I don't know how you manage, Emmett, but you have a positive genius for putting things in such a way . . .

EMMETT (*Astonished*) What are you talking about? What did I say? (*Rises. Appeals to* FRANK) Did I say anything, Mr. Michaelson?

FRANK I . . .
(FRANK *looks at him. How can he tell him briefly, tersely, the workings of the female mind? Finally, just gestures helplessly with both hands*)

MOLLIE Thank you for the flowers, Emmett, and thank you for the invitation, but I'm completely exhausted.

EMMETT Oh? Okay. (*Moves the flowers to* MOLLIE) Gee, Mollie—(*Picks up his hat*) this isn't the way I wanted it to happen. I've been thinking about this for months.

MOLLIE It's all right, Emmett. Really it is. I'll see you.

EMMETT (*Considers this an opening*) What are you doing a week from tonight?
    (FRANK *has given up all pretense of not listening; he watches with fascination*)

MOLLIE A week from tonight?

EMMETT (*Quickly*) You couldn't possibly have a date. You just got here.

MOLLIE (*Resigned*) All right. I couldn't possibly have a date. What did you have in mind?

EMMETT (*Sits on the couch. Inventing—not too skillfully*) Well, there's this . . . my uncle and aunt are here from Denver . . . and they're throwing this big party at the Beverly Hilton Hotel for my jerk cousin . . . who's transferring to U.C.L.A.

MOLLIE Oh.

EMMETT (*Hastily. A deep breath*) First we have to go to their suite and have cocktails.

MOLLIE All right. Is it formal?

EMMETT No, no. Very *in*formal.

MOLLIE At the Beverly Hilton? Are you sure, Emmett?

EMMETT Positive. I'm in charge of all the arrangements. (*Rises. Crosses to door*) See you Friday.
    (*He is out*)

MOLLIE (*Gestures dramatically in the direction of the departed* EMMETT) There! Do I have to submit any more evidence to prove my case?

FRANK   Case? What case are you talking about?

MOLLIE   People just take a longer time to mature in the West, that's all.

FRANK   (*Rises. Crosses to* MOLLIE)   Oh, Mollie, the kid's just trying too hard. He's working like a dog trying to impress you. (*Puts the flowers upstage*) He's been counting the days until you got home. The minutes, judging by the way he popped in here. (*She softens a little.* FRANK *sits on the couch*) Why do you suppose he's driving that florist's truck? (*Pleading* EMMETT's *case earnestly*) He wants to make money so he can spend it all on you! You'll probably have a great time Friday night. He's bright, he's interesting. Of course when he's with you, he acts like an absolute idiot. He's so smitten, all the wrong words come out of his mouth. But if you give him half a chance ...

MOLLIE   (*Kisses* FRANK's *hand*)   All right, Daddy, all right.
         (*She gets up*)

FRANK   I have a hunch about him, Mollie. He's going to be somebody.
         (LIZ *comes down steps*)

LIZ   What did the creep want?

MOLLIE   (*Shrugs, goes toward the stairs*)   Oh, he's taking me to some party at the Beverly Hilton. I really don't want to go, but I'd hate to have people out here thinking of me as a snob.
         (*She exits.* FRANK *and* LIZ *look after her for a moment*)

FRANK   (*Resolutely*)   I won't think of her as a snob. I don't know what I *will* think of her as, but I won't think of her as a snob.

LIZ (*Crosses to* FRANK *and hugs him*) Oh, Daddy! You're such a dreamer!

> (*The lights go out in the Michaelson living room. A dressing table appears left center. Its back is to the audience and* ANNE *is seated at it, peering through the mirrorless frame of the table at the audience. She is in evening clothes and is evidently planning to attend a bal de tête, for she is making the final adjustments to a small papier-mâché Christmas tree which she has fixed on her head. It is quite becoming.* LIZ's *voice is heard from offstage*)

LIZ's VOICE Where are you, Mom?

ANNE I'm upstairs, dear.

> (*She adjusts a pin in her headdress. In a moment,* LIZ *comes in, dressed for bowling, holding a star made of aluminum foil*)

LIZ (*Holds out the star*) See, Mother. It worked. Out of aluminum foil. Look how nice that star came out.

ANNE Well, aren't you smart. Thank you, darling.

> (LIZ *fixes it on top of the headdress arrangement*)

LIZ You know they can't miss having a fight.

ANNE Who?

LIZ Mollie and Emmett. Did you see the way she greeted him? (*Very snooty, imitating* MOLLIE) How *are* you this evening, Emmett?

ANNE (*With a slight smile*) Patience, Liz, patience.

LIZ What ever happened to "Hi, Emmett"?

ANNE Liz, she'll never again be as old as she is right now. Not if she lives to be a hundred. What time will you be home?

LIZ Well . . . bowling . . . then everybody's bound to be hungry . . . Oh, about twelve.

ANNE No later.

LIZ I'm doubling, Mother, so I'll just have to do the best I can. (*There is the sound of a horn honking outside*) Oh, God! I wish I were old enough to go with someone who rings the doorbell instead of honking! (*The honk is repeated*) I'm coming! I'm coming! Night, Mom. (*Kisses her mother, calls as she runs off*) Night, Daddy.

FRANK'S VOICE Night, sweetie!
(*He comes in, only partly dressed for a black-tie party. He finishes his dressing onstage, taking in* ANNE'S *headgear*)

FRANK Hey. I had no idea you were going to be that elaborate.

ANNE (*Working on her appearance*) I hadn't planned to, but Millie Crowder has been working on hers for a week. She's got a whole Chinese village on her head. (*Makes a final adjustment and rises*) There! (FRANK *says nothing; he's too busy with himself in the mirror*) Well, for heaven's sake, say if you like it or not. Do you realize how much work I . . .

FRANK (*Hastily*) I'm mad about it. I might even vote for you, if you're terribly nice to me afterward.
(*They kiss*)

ANNE Oh, sure.
(FRANK *nods and studies himself in mirror, as he finishes dressing*)

FRANK You know, when my father was my age I used to think he was old. But I feel kind of snappy tonight.

ANNE Now sit down and I'll do you.

FRANK (*Appalled*) Wait a minute. If you think I'm going to put something like that on my . . .

ANNE (*Pushes him into the seat*) I worked out something very simple. (*She picks up a Turkish towel*) If people are giving a *bal de tête*, everybody has to go along with it or it's no fun.

FRANK (*Suspiciously*) What am I going to be?

ANNE A sheik.

FRANK (*Looks at himself in the mirror*) With that face?
(*He makes a grimace*)

ANNE (*Calmly, adjusting his headgear*) You're a member of a different tribe from Rudolph Valentino.

FRANK The ugly tribe.

ANNE Now hold still.
(*He looks up at her*)

FRANK Annie, you look beautiful.
(*He holds her around the waist a moment*)

ANNE Thank you.

FRANK (*Turns to the mirror again*) And didn't Mollie look pretty tonight?

ANNE Mmm-hmmm ...
(*She is tying a cord around the towel to try to get the proper effect*)

FRANK And Emmett ... I almost didn't recognize him. He really looked ... well (*He can't go too far*) ... bearable.

ANNE (*Completes her work*) There! How do you like it?
(*She looks at* FRANK. *He studies himself in the mirror from various angles*)

FRANK (*Flatly*) I look exactly like a man with a towel on his head.
(*They both look up sharply as* MOLLIE'S *voice is heard from downstairs*)

MOLLIE Daddy! Mom!
(FRANK *and* ANNE *exchange a puzzled look*)

FRANK Mollie? What's she doing home?

MOLLIE Would you come down, please?

ANNE Something's wrong!
(FRANK *and* ANNE *both run off. Lights go out. The Michaelson living room rolls on in the darkness.* WHITMYER *is heard talking on the telephone*)

WHITMYER Yes, dear. Everything's under control ... Angel, stop worrying. I took care of everything ... She's all right. He's all right ... (*By now, the lights are on in the living room and reveal* MOLLIE, EMMETT, *and* EMMETT'S *father;* MR.

WHITMYER *is talking into the phone.* MOLLIE *and* EMMETT *are both in party attire.* MOLLIE *is at the foot of the steps, looking furious.* EMMETT, *very hangdog, stands beside his father.* MR. WHITMYER *is a small, energetic man whose face is very red just now*) No, no. No police, and nothing will be in the newspapers ... Of course he's all right ... I'll let you talk to him. (*Holds out the phone to* EMMETT *but doesn't let go of it*) Here! Say hello to your mother!

EMMETT (*Weakly, into the mouthpiece*) Hello, Mom. I'm ...

WHITMYER (*Puts phone back to his own ear*) Your precious little darling is fine, see? We'll be home right away.
(MR. WHITMYER *hangs up as* ANNE *and* FRANK *are seen coming down the steps*)

MOLLIE Mother and Daddy, I want you to meet Mr. Whitmyer. (*Points to* EMMETT) That monster's father!
(FRANK *and* ANNE *move forward and say nothing, waiting for a clue*)

WHITMYER How do you do. (*To* EMMETT, *sternly*) You're going to apologize to Mr. and Mrs. Michaelson, and then I'm going to take you home and ... (*Breaks off*) I wish you weren't too big to thrash!
(*He pushes* EMMETT *roughly to a position between* FRANK *and himself*)

EMMETT (*Mumbling*) I apologize.

FRANK What for?

WHITMYER Go on! Tell these decent people what for!

EMMETT I apologize for . . . (*Stops short*) I can't say it!
(*He turns his back and stumbles to a position behind his father*)

MOLLIE Well, I can! He apologizes for trying to attack me in the Beverly Hilton Hotel!

FRANK What?

MOLLIE That party with his cousins from Denver! They don't exist! He made it all up. He and I were the only ones at the party! He rented the room! (*Sits on the couch, looks at her father*) And you said I wasn't being nice to Emmett. I was being too tough. Well, next time he wants a date, *you* go with him!

FRANK Well, he's not too big for me to thrash! (*Starts after* EMMETT. EMMETT *uses his father as a shield and retreats stage right.* WHITMYER *is getting mauled by him and* FRANK *in the process, as* ANNE *gets in the middle*)

ANNE (*Holding* FRANK *back*) Frank, Mollie said he only *tried*. Nothing happened.

WHITMYER Fortunately. Fortunately for all of us the assistant manager of the hotel is a friend of mine.

FRANK I don't see anything fortunate about anything in this whole business!
(WHITMYER *retreats*)

WHITMYER Well, anyway, they were seen going up in the elevator. This manager friend of mine had the house detective bring them down to his office. And instead of calling the police, he called me. Tell them what name you registered under!

EMMETT (*In a very small voice*) John Keats.

WHITMYER (*Stands between* MOLLIE *and* EMMETT) Mr. and Mrs. John Keats! See? No ordinary boy. You and your goddam poetry! (*Pushes* EMMETT. EMMETT *trips over the hassock and falls down. Back to* FRANK *and* ANNE) Number one in his class. Straight A's. Already admitted to four colleges, including Harvard . . .

MOLLIE Oh, no!

WHITMYER (*Riding through*) And this is what he uses his genius for! (*Very abjectly*) I couldn't be more sorry. We've all known about Mollie for years. Emmett's told us how brilliant and wonderful she is . . . (*Sees* EMMETT *is still on the floor*) Stand up, boy. (EMMETT *gets to his feet*) Lucky that man was a friend of mine or we'd all be at the police station right now. (*Looks at* FRANK *across room, takes in headdress for the first time*) Have you got a headache?

FRANK What? (*After a moment, he remembers*) Oh, for God's sake! I forgot all about this.
  (*He pulls the towel off his head, makes a ball of it, and flings it at* ANNE, *as if she were somehow at fault. She catches it*)

ANNE (*Crosses to* EMMETT) Emmett, how could you? I mean, all the years you've been coming to our house. How could you?

EMMETT (*On the verge of tears*) Mrs. Michaelson, you know how I love Mollie. And . . . well . . . Mr. Michaelson told me she's been getting permission to spend weekends (FRANK *looks around*) at Dartmouth with other guys . . . and Yale—

(ANNE *and* MOLLIE *both look at* FRANK, *surprised*) too . . . and I just wanted to prove I'm as good as they are.

FRANK (*Cutting him off*) If I were you, Emmett, I'd shut up about what I was trying to prove!

EMMETT But Mollie still thinks of me as a little kid, and I'm just as . . .

WHITMYER (*Also cutting him off*) Mr. Michaelson is right. Shut up, boy! It's the smart ones who cause all the trouble.

FRANK Mr. Whitmyer, do me a favor, take him away. Please take him away, because if I ever get my hands on him, you're going to have a son entering Forest Lawn—not Harvard!

WHITMYER (*Pushes* EMMETT *toward the door*) Go on, son. I'm going to take him home, and tomorrow morning, I'm going to sell his car!

EMMETT Oh, Dad!
    (*They go out*)

FRANK And I used to feel sorry for the little bastard—standing across the street looking up at your window. Mollie, I must apologize. Apparently, I'm responsible for your having a thoroughly humiliating experience.

MOLLIE Oh, I'm not really marred. Takes more than that to mar me. (*Rises*) In some ways it was kind of funny. (*Crosses*) By the time I get back to school I'll reappraise it and it'll be a hilarious story to tell the girls.
    (*She sits on the hassock*)

FRANK (*Crosses to* MOLLIE) But I was so wrong . . .

MOLLIE Of course you were. It isn't anything you know anything about. I may not have learned much scholastically, but I did learn about men. Some are safe and some are unsafe. Emmett is unsafe.

(FRANK *looks very unhappy*)

ANNE (*Helpfully*) It's important to learn about that, too, Frank.

(*Hands* FRANK *the towel*)

FRANK (*Sunk*) Of course. (*Looks at his watch*) We're late for the party, huh? (*A look at* MOLLIE) I . . . er . . . er . . . is it all right to leave her alone?

MOLLIE What are you going to do? Get a sitter for me?

FRANK I guess not. (*To* ANNE) Coming?

(ANNE *nods, and goes toward the stairs, stopping a moment to rest a comforting hand on* MOLLIE's *shoulder. The phone rings.* FRANK *picks it up*)

FRANK Hello? . . . Yes, she's here. Just a moment. (*To* MOLLIE) For you. Long distance.

(MOLLIE *hurries to take the phone, and* ANNE *continues on upstairs for her wrap*)

MOLLIE (*Into the phone*) Hello? . . . Yes, this is she . . . (*Her voice is suddenly warm and vibrant*) Donn? . . . (*She sits on the couch*) Donn! How wonderful! . . . Are you having a great vacation? . . . Oh? . . . (FRANK *crosses to the bar, his back to the audience. World-weary*) Yes, isn't it the truth . . . Just about the same here . . . Oh, nothing very much, except something awfully funny just happened. You'll panic when I tell you about it. Absolute riot . . . You don't know it, Donn, but you're involved with a femme fatale . . . Mmmmmmmm . . . Mmmmmmmmmm . . . (*She giggles*) Er . . . er . . . (*Before she can look at* FRANK, *he realizes he is eavesdropping and goes into hall*) Well, of course, I miss you too, darling. Terribly . . . Oh, they're wonderful, but I don't even feel as if I belong here any more. I just didn't realize how *provincial* . . . It's really sort of sad . . . Oh? . . . Sounds marvelous . . . (*Slowly*) I don't know what my folks'll say . . . I'll ask. They might . . . Well, I'll let you know in plenty of time . . . Look, this is costing you a fortune. Goodbye, darling . . . Of course I do . . . Good-bye . . .

(*She hangs up. After a moment,* FRANK *returns*)

FRANK (*Tentatively*) How's . . . how's Donn?

MOLLIE Oh, he's wonderful.

FRANK So I gather.
(*There is a pause*)

MOLLIE (*Also tentatively*) Daddy . . .
(*She rises*)

FRANK Yes?

MOLLIE Donn invited me to spend New Year's Eve in New York, and it would only mean leaving two or three days earlier . . . Would you and Mother mind?
(*She looks at* FRANK)

FRANK (*Crosses to the couch and sits. After a moment*) I was under the impression you just got here.

MOLLIE (*Sits*) I've been here seven days already!

FRANK (*Another moment to take it in*) Seven whole days.

MOLLIE Well, I wouldn't be leaving till next week. And it's New Year's Eve in New York, and who is there for me to go out with here?

FRANK Yes. That's very important.

MOLLIE Oh!
(*She looks upset; turns away from him*)

FRANK I'm not being flip, Mollie. It's very depressing to stay home New Year's Eve. Almost as depressing as going out.

MOLLIE Well then?

FRANK (*Gives up*) Why don't you take it up with your mother? (*Turns away*) I don't feel entirely qualified. She's the one who gives permissions. Whatever you two decide. (*There is an awkward pause*)

MOLLIE What's the matter?

FRANK Nothing. Nothing's the matter.

MOLLIE (*Looks at* FRANK) Oh, I can read you like a book. I could when I was four, and I still can. (*Looks away from him. A moment*) You're terribly disappointed in me, aren't you? You expect me to be Eleanor Roosevelt or Madame Curie—and I'm not.

FRANK (*Turns to* MOLLIE) I don't want Madame Curie. I just want you to be the best you can.

MOLLIE Has it occurred to you that this might be the best I can? And if that's so, what's wrong with it? Is it wrong to want to be liked and accepted?

Art Carney, Phyllis Thaxter, Elizabeth Ashley, and June Harding as FRANK MICHAELSON, ANNE MICHAELSON, MOLLIE MICHAELSON, and LIZ MICHAELSON

FRANK I'm not talking about conformity and nonconformity. I'm talking about you. And to see you *settle* for this . . . Yes, when I see what's important to you, I *am* disappointed.

MOLLIE Daddy, I'm a perfectly ordinary girl. Why don't you face it?

FRANK (*Very gently*) Mollie, I've known you a long time. I know your potential. I know your capabilities. It's so much more than this. You know that, don't you?

MOLLIE (*Shakes her head. Rises*) Yes.

FRANK Couldn't you give it another try?
          (MOLLIE *softens, affected by the seriousness of his tone*)

MOLLIE I don't know what star you want me to reach for.

FRANK Neither do I. But I know you have it in you to be something wonderful. You just have to work at it.

MOLLIE (*After a moment*) I'll try. (FRANK *gets up and goes to her*) And I'll begin by spending New Year's Eve in California.

FRANK That's my girl.
          (MOLLIE *throws her arms around her father's neck. He holds her*)

MOLLIE Oh, Daddy! I'm never going to love anybody as much as you love me. It must hurt like hell!
          (*As they stand in close embrace*)
                    Curtain

ACT TWO

Time: Now.

At rise: FRANK *is seen, stage right, leaning one arm on the telephone pole and looking out at the audience. He has the air of a man who has been through a great deal, and is engrossed in thought.*

FRANK   The first year is supposed to be the hardest—but I think that's only true of marriage. (*Sighs deeply*) Anyway, we're now in our sophomore year, and Hawthorne College, having done such a brilliant job on Mollie the first year— as you saw—rewarded itself by raising the tuition. I complained bitterly to Annie—and mailed the check. (*Smiles wryly*) Money doesn't stop us. We're determined to be educated. (*Changes, takes on the manner of an orator*) We put behind us the bubble hair, the dry martini, and the word "fabulous," and we moved into a new phase. We became socially conscious. (*Thinks about it for a moment*) Of course, that was what I was pulling for all the time, but Mollie has a way of going all out that . . . (*Stops, shakes his head*) For example, she marched up and down outside the British Consulate in Boston shouting "Free Bertrand Russell." Of course he'd been let out of jail two weeks before— but that really wasn't the point. She busted up her romance with Donn when she discovered he was for Barry Goldwater. She also spearheaded a drive demanding to know on what basis the faculty had turned down the drama club's decision to do *Lady Chatterley's Lover* as its attraction for the father-daughter weekend. This was resolved when the dean explained she thought the students were mature enough— but she wasn't so sure about the fathers. (*A pause*) And then in the second half of her sophomore year, Mollie wrote us that she probably wouldn't be home that summer. She had applied for a job with the State Department to work overseas. (FRANK *beams. This he approves of*) She took a test, and in answer to the question, "Do you have any preference as to the kind of work you will do or where you will be sent?" She answered, "Anything, any place, as long as it helps the cause of peace." (*His grin broadens*) How about that?

(FRANK *disappears, and the lights come up on the dormitory room.* MOLLIE, *on the desk chair, and a lusty young female named* LINDA LEHMAN, *on the bed, are twanging their guitars with great gusto.* SARAH *and* ADELE *sit on other bed. All are singing "Tseiner." This is an Israeli song which is played and sung with spirit and audience participation in the way of handclapping.* SARAH *and* ADELE *supply the handclapping. All apparently have been affected by the socially conscious phase, which is evidenced in an utter disregard for what they are wearing and what the hair fashion is that particular year. Stark simplicity is the order of the day. "Tseiner" comes to an end. They wind up with a flourish, out of breath and fired with zeal*)

MOLLIE   Oh, Linda! You're so lucky to be Jewish!

LINDA   (*Astonished*) That's a switch. I always heard it the other way round.

MOLLIE   Well, all the people we admire are Jewish.

74

SARAH That's right, Mort Sahl, Sigmund Freud ...

ADELE Salinger—The *New Yorker* one, I mean.

MOLLIE Adlai Stevenson!

LINDA Who?

MOLLIE Of course he's not, but he really is—if you know what I mean.

SARAH Certainly.

LINDA Oh, you girls are absurd, the next thing you'll want to spend your third year in Israel dancing the Hora.

SARAH I'd love to. I find Jewish men fascinating. (*Dreamily*) Leonard Bernstein! He could conduct me any place.

LINDA Oh, you're just picking isolated examples.
       (*The phone rings.* MOLLIE *picks it up*)

MOLLIE Shalom! Who's this? Oh, hi. This is Mollie. Linda's right here. (*Holds out the phone to* LINDA) Clancy Sussman.

LINDA Yes, Clancy ... You're kidding! ... You signed the lease for the coffee house ... Tremont Street! You'll be rolling in money ... What are you going to call it? "The Manic Depressive?" ... That sounds so commonplace ... Certainly, Clancy, I'll be there opening night with my guitar clutched in my hot little hand ... Oh? Well, I'll ask her ... Call you back ... Good-bye, Mr. Sussman. (*Hangs up*) Well, what do you know? Clancy's really going to open a coffee house.

SARAH But Linda, how much can you make out of a coffee house? It's just coffee and ...

LINDA Oh, Clancy's putting in a full menu.

MOLLIE Anything Clancy Sussman turns his hand to is bound to succeed. I just have that feeling about him. (*The phone rings. She picks it up*) Yes. Who's speaking? (*Her voice turns to ice*) No, Emmett, I will not fix you up with another girl! Not after your behavior last time! Jennifer was furious with me for having suggested you. Even by the loose standards around here, you're a sex maniac! Why don't you take up some reasonable vice, like ... like dope ... or alcohol ... or ... or boys? And do me a favor, Emmett: Lose my phone number!
     (*She bangs down the telephone*)

ADELE Well, you certainly chopped him.

LINDA Mollie, how would you like to make seven dollars a night—twice a week? (MOLLIE *looks at her*) Clancy has this brilliant idea of having folk singing every Friday and Saturday night. We're what Clancy calls "ambiance."

MOLLIE Ambiance? (*Still wary*) What kind of songs will we sing?

LINDA Oh, you know. Ballads and things. (*Picks up guitar and plays and sings*)
          "My father was hung for sheep stealing
          My mother was burned for a witch
          My sister's a bawdy-house keeper
          And I'm a son of a ..."
     (*All the girls join in here*)

ALL (*Singing*)
Fa-la-la-la-la-la Fa-la-la-la-la-la-
Fa-la-la-la-la-la Fa-la-la-laaaaaaaaah.

> (*On the last syllable of the song, the dormitory is off, and the Michaelson living room is on, with* FRANK *seated on the couch, holding a letter, and* ANNE *beside him, consulting the dictionary*)

ANNE   Ambiance. Here it is. (*Reading*) "Environment; surroundings; especially in decorative art. The totality of motifs or accessories surrounding and enhancing the central motif."

> (*She and* FRANK *exchange a puzzled look*)

FRANK   She has the damnedest extracurricular activities I ever heard of. (*Returns to the letter as to something distasteful*) "Clancy Sussman is really some kind of genius, not only in school but in the financial world as well. While every other night spot in town is half empty, 'The Sleeping Pill' is always jammed . . ." (FRANK *looks at* ANNE) "Except, that is . . . not lately. The trouble is Clancy is quite mad and absolutely unpredictable. If Gerry Mulligan is in town he simply doesn't show up to open the place."

ANNE   Who's Gerry Mulligan?

FRANK   Baseball player.

ANNE   Oh!

FRANK   (*Continues letter*) "I haven't heard yet on the European deal for this summer but Adele's sister says they always take time. Everybody in my poetry class has developed a mad crush on our professor. But (ho-ho) he seems to have

77

eyes only for me. I'm doing my term paper on T. S. Eliot and we've had really inspirational conferences about it. The campus gossip is that he's divorced and I wouldn't be surprised. He has such a hurt look about the eyes. Makes you want to take care of him . . . It will probably be the best thing I've ever done."

ANNE   What?

FRANK   The paper . . . I think.

ANNE   Well, does it say that?

FRANK   No, it just says it'll probably be the best thing she's ever done. Does everybody go through this?

ANNE   I guess so. It's the price you pay.

FRANK   For what?

ANNE   I don't know. You just pay it.

FRANK   "Anyway, folks, you know where I am every Friday and Saturday night. Daddy if you were planning to come for father-daughter weekend, you could hear us in person, but since you're not I've sent you a record we made so you'll know how we sound. Please make allowances for the acoustics, 'The Sleeping Pill' used to be a bowling alley. Love, Mollie." Maybe I'd *better* go up there for father-daughter weekend.

ANNE   Oh sure. Five hundred dollars to see your daughter for two days?
     (FRANK *picks up the flat package and goes to the record player as he opens it*)

78

FRANK (*Hopefully*) Maybe it broke. (*Looking at the record*)
Nope. Not even a scratch. (*He drops it on the record player*)
Well, bombs away!

> (*He switches on the machine. In a moment, a horrible
> noise comes out—wailing, doleful, a little like very slow
> bagpipe music.* FRANK *looks at the record in horror.*
> ANNE *gets up and goes to the machine*)

ANNE You had it on the wrong speed. (*She adjusts it, and a
guitar accompaniment is heard playing normally. In a moment,* MOLLIE's *and* LINDA's *voices are heard singing*) You
see? That's not *too* terrible.

> (FRANK *gestures her to silence, and they both listen with
> enjoyment,* ANNE *settling in the chair beside the player
> and* FRANK *leaning against the banister and even doing a
> little directing*)

MOLLIE'S AND LINDA'S VOICES
  "Here's to the girl who steals a kiss and stays to steal another,
  Here's to the girl who steals a kiss and stays to steal another,
  She's a joy to all mankind
  She's a joy to all mankind
  She's a joy to all mankind
  And she'll soon be a mother!"

> (*They are both stunned for a moment, then* ANNE *gets
> up and goes to* FRANK)

ANNE You go up there, Frank! I don't care what it costs—you
go up there!

> (FRANK *nods his agreement, and the living room disap-
> pears. "The Sleeping Pill" comes on, stage center, tables
> and chairs, dimly lit by candlelight.* LINDA *and* MOLLIE
> *are seated on high stools, playing their guitars and sing-*

ing "The Tattooed Lady." They wear peasant dresses and strings of beads. CLANCY SUSSMAN *is seated at a table, reading a book.* CLANCY *is a tall, thin young man, who slouches rather than walks. He looks as if he has never had enough to eat)*

LINDA AND MOLLIE (*Singing*)
>"I paid a dime to see
>The tattooed lady
>Tattooed from head to toe.
>That's quite a sight you know.
>And over on one thigh
>Was a British Man o' War."

CLANCY (*Waving to an imaginary customer*)   Good night Ed, come again.

LINDA AND MOLLIE
>"And across her back
>Was a Union Jack
>Now who could ask for more.
>And up and down her spine
>Ran the Mason-Dixon line.
>And in a certain spot
>Ooo—oo
>Was a blue forget-me-not.
>And over on one kidney
>Was a bird's eye view
>Of Sidney.
>But what I like best
>Right across her chest
>Was my home in Tennessee."

(*They finish the number to a very thin spatter of applause, and take their bows very unprofessionally*)

MOLLIE I think there are six customers in here.

LINDA I counted eight.
(CLANCY *comes to them, applauding, though he is the only one*)

LINDA Are we doing better, Clancy?

CLANCY (*Arms around their shoulders*) We're going to make it. Don't let them get you down. Just keep pitching. You're my rod and my staff and my good right arm. (*Now brisk*) Look, will you hop to it and lend a hand in the kitchen? We're running out of coffee cups.
(LINDA *crosses to do his bidding*)

MOLLIE What happened to the dish washer?

CLANCY He insulted the racial origins of the cook. Of course I couldn't let him stay after that—not Clancy Sussman.

LINDA Of course not.

MOLLIE How disgusting.

CLANCY You're the only ones in my world I can really count on. Even the Danish-pastry man let me down today.

MOLLIE Yes, but he was here last week when you weren't. He was stuck with all that stuff.

LINDA That's not very sound business, Clancy.

CLANCY Well, let's not worry about him. Now hurry, will you? Clear those tables first.
(CLANCY *goes off with the guitars, as* MOLLIE *and* LINDA *start to clear the tables*)

LINDA (*Thoughtfully*) The most extraordinary thing. Every dish washer Clancy ever hires is guilty of race prejudice.

MOLLIE Linda, were you paid last week?

LINDA No. Were you?

MOLLIE No. And I have a feeling the dish washer wasn't either. You know, very often that sort of thing can lead to race prejudice.
  (*The girls disappear into the kitchen with the dishes. In a moment, ALEX comes in and peers around blindly in the gloom. ALEX has grown up considerably since we first met him, both in appearance and manner. CLANCY spots him and approaches*)

ALEX Hi, Clancy . . .
  (*Even CLANCY can't see too well*)

CLANCY Oh, Alex Loomis. Hi. You all alone?

ALEX Yes, of course. What the hell have you done to the lighting in here?

CLANCY (*Ushering him to a table*) Well, the New England Gas and Light Company and I are having a slight disagreement. I can read a meter, too. I didn't take all that science for nothing. (*Holds a chair for ALEX*) They've been making patsies out of the consumers for years. So I just put my foot down.

ALEX And they put the lights out. (*Looks around*) Where are the Bobbsey twins?

CLANCY (*With aplomb*) They're back in their dressing room
—resting. (*Picks up menu*) You just missed them. (*Waves
to an imaginary customer who is leaving*) Good night, Joe.
Come again. (*Back to* ALEX) Want to see a menu? (*He
hands* ALEX *a menu, then lights a small pencil flashlight and
holds it so that* ALEX *can read*) The Danish pastry is gone,
we're out of hamburgers, and coffee is twenty cents tonight.

ALEX Mine genial host, I really didn't drop in for coffee. I'm
doing free-lance journalism, and I think there's a story in
this place—you, the girls, how to become independently
wealthy while still an undergraduate.

CLANCY Independently wealthy! Ha, ha—All right. I'll give
you a story. (*Yells toward kitchen*) Hey, kids! Two large
coffees and a pizza!

MOLLIE (*Offstage*) Coming up!

CLANCY (*Sits*) Alex, when I opened this place, my idea was
to have the equivalent of the country store—a Paris bistro in
the middle of Boston—a stimulus to the free-and-easy exchange of ideas. Put that down on a piece of paper and take
it to the bank and see what kind of credit you get! Their
grubby little minds are interested only in the dollar. *People*
don't matter. Let me tell you something, Alex, certain
moneyed interests are out to get me!
   (ALEX *is looking at* CLANCY, *fascinated*)

ALEX Clancy, you're crazy.
   (MOLLIE *comes in, carrying a tray with two coffee cups
   and an order of pizza. She and* ALEX *exchange imper-
   sonal greetings as she hands out the food quite inef-
   ficiently*)

83

MOLLIE That's the last of the pizza.

CLANCY (*Gets up, outraged. The whole world is against him*)
The pizza man didn't show either?

MOLLIE Nope.

CLANCY (*To* ALEX) You see what I mean?

ALEX (*Looks at the pizza doubtfully*) Is that last night's?

MOLLIE (*Matter-of-factly*) We weren't open last night.
    (ALEX *pushes the pizza away slowly with his hand*)

CLANCY What are you pushing it away for?

ALEX Who pushed it? It moved by itself.
    (MOLLIE *laughs*)

CLANCY Thanks, baby. Loomis here wants to interview you
later, for the papers. (*He pats her on the fanny. She slaps his
hand away, and goes.* CLANCY *crosses left*) You used to date
Mollie, didn't you? What happened?

ALEX When I used to date Mollie, I was as obnoxious as you
are now—and she told me so.

CLANCY Ha, ha. (FRANK, *looking different from his California
self in overcoat and hat, comes in and stumbles in the darkness*) Excuse me. There's a customer.
    (FRANK *bumps into a table.* CLANCY *reaches him in time
    to steady him*)

FRANK (*Uncertainly*) Are you ... er ... open?

CLANCY (*Grandly*) Do you have a reservation?

FRANK   I tried to call, but they told me the phone was disconnected.

CLANCY   (*To* ALEX)   Hear that, Alex? They'll stop at nothing.

FRANK   I beg your pardon.

CLANCY   (*Smoothly*)   It just so happens that I can seat you. Here.
(CLANCY *seats* FRANK *at a table next to* ALEX'S, *hands him the menu and holds the flashlight*)

FRANK   Thank you.

CLANCY   (*Laconically*)   No Danish pastry, no hamburgers.

ALEX   (*Sotto voce*)   And no pizza.

CLANCY   Just coffee.

FRANK   (*Attempting humor*)   In that case I won't need my Diners' Club card.

CLANCY   We don't honor Diners' Club cards.

FRANK   You don't?

CLANCY   They're inflationary. What'll you have?

FRANK   I put myself in your hands. Whatever you decide.
(CLANCY *starts off, has an idea. He stops at* ALEX'S *table and goes into a whispered conference about the pizza.* ALEX *shrugs.* CLANCY *picks up the pizza and brings it to* FRANK)

CLANCY Aaah, we're in luck. My friend here was just about to start on his third order, when he realized he'd overestimated his appetite. And so . . . you might as well pay for it.

FRANK Oh good. (*To* ALEX) Thank you. I'm just off a plane from California and I'm really starved.

ALEX (*Not at all sure*) It's quite all right.
       (CLANCY *shambles off.* FRANK *turns his attention to the pizza. First he picks up his fork and works away, realizes he is getting nowhere. Then he takes the knife and attacks it, sawing away ineffectually. Studies the problem a moment. He looks around to be sure nobody is watching, then picks up the pizza and tries to tear it. This gets him nowhere. Finally he gives up, wipes his hands on napkin. He looks at* ALEX)

FRANK I beg your pardon. Did I hear correctly? Did you really eat two of these?

ALEX (*Shakes his head*) Accordng to the *Harvard Crimson,* Duncan Hines ate his last meal here.

FRANK Oh. (*Settles back*) In that case, I'll just wait for the floor show.

ALEX The what?

FRANK The floor show. There's a floor show isn't there?

ALEX Oh! Oh, the two girls.

FRANK Yes, I'll just wait and see them.

ALEX (*Doubtfully*) Oh.

FRANK (*Takes a moment*) Are they that bad?

ALEX Well, frankly . . .

FRANK (*Cutting him off*) Please, no! I haven't got the strength for a frank opinion. Before you go any further, I ought to tell you one of them is my daughter.

ALEX You're Mr. Michaelson.

FRANK How did you know?

ALEX Well, I've taken Mollie out and I know she's from California—and the other one isn't. (*Hitching his chair closer*) I'm Alex Loomis.
(*They shake hands*)

FRANK How do you do?
(LINDA *comes out of the kitchen and sets a coffee cup in front of* FRANK)

LINDA (*A statement*) You don't want cream and sugar, do you.

FRANK (*Intimidated*) No. I guess I don't.
(LINDA *starts off*)

ALEX (*Rises*) Linda, where's Mollie?

LINDA She's in the kitchen washing the dishes.
(*She goes.* FRANK *stares after her, then turns to look at* ALEX)

ALEX (*Sits*) Don't look so pained, Mr. Michaelson. At Bennington dishwashing is a three-credit course.
(FRANK *sighs and has some coffee. Looks surprised*)

87

FRANK This coffee's all right!

ALEX It's instant. What can they do to it? Mr. Michaelson, I hope I didn't give you the wrong impression about the girls. They're not too bad. They're just going through a stage, but it's nothing you have to go into hiding about. They'll get over it.

FRANK Say that again! The first part.

ALEX I said they're just going through a stage.

FRANK That's exactly what I've been saying! All the way across on the plane I kept saying "That's all it is—a stage." It's very interesting that that's been your observation too.

ALEX It's easy for me to see it now. I've been through it. When I was a sophomore, I went home for Christmas and I gave my father—a nervous breakdown.

FRANK How is your father now?

ALEX He was making very good progress, but my kid brother started Princeton this year, and . . .

FRANK (*Nods his understanding*) Tell me honestly, don't you think these kids are a little nuttier than they have to be?

ALEX No. Not really. You see, your generation expects this generation to save the world. You keep watching us. Everybody expects us to be scientists or specialists, which we're perfectly willing to be. But after seven or eight years of all that going to school, what's the first thing you do with us? You clap us in the Army. All that training to become a Private First Class!

FRANK Then according to you, we ought to be grateful you're not twice as nutty as you are?

ALEX I think so.
(MOLLIE *comes scuttling out of the kitchen, wearing a large apron over her dress. She slides into a seat beside* ALEX)

MOLLIE Alex, do you mind if I sit with you and pretend I'm a date?

ALEX What's Clancy up to now? Got you mingling with the customers?

MOLLIE No, no. There's a city inspector out in the kitchen giving Clancy a terrible time. Linda's hiding in the broom closet. You see, neither one of us is a licensed food handler!

FRANK Thank God!

MOLLIE I beg your pardon?

FRANK I said thank God you're not a licensed food handler!

MOLLIE (*Gets up*) Daddy! What are you doing here?

FRANK (*Stands up, too*) It's father-daughter weekend, so I know what I'm doing here. But the question nobody'll ever be able to answer is—what the hell are *you* doing here?
(*As he gestures her out of the coffee shop, the lights go out. The lights come up on a bare stage (the green of the campus). It is early morning, and the chapel bells are heard ringing. After a moment,* FRANK *comes in and looks around, apparently lost. He stops an imaginary girl who is walking past*)

FRANK I beg your pardon, but I'm going to classes with my daughter this morning, and she told me to meet her outside of Spencer Hall. I wonder if you could . . . (*Listens*) Oh, I'm standing right in front of it? Thank you very much.
(*The girl evidently goes on her way.* MOLLIE, *in a loose coat thrown over her dress, books in her arms, enters*)

MOLLIE Hi, Daddy.

FRANK Morning, dear. We're not late, are we?

MOLLIE No. We have a few minutes yet. I'm so glad you're here.

FRANK Where did you think I'd be?

MOLLIE After last night—maybe on the plane back to California.

FRANK No. I'm anxious to see what the academic side of life in the East is like.

MOLLIE (*Her head on his shoulder*) Honorable daughter admits coffee house very bad mistake.

FRANK Honorable father agrees.
(*The bells are heard ringing the hour*)

MOLLIE Time for class, Daddy.
(*They start off right*)

FRANK What class is it?

MOLLIE English Twenty. Modern Poetry. Mr. Hibbetts.

FRANK The one you wrote us about.

MOLLIE Yes.

FRANK The one with the hurt look.

MOLLIE You'll just love him.

FRANK Oh, I have very deep feelings about him already.

(*They link arms and go off. Stage center, a classroom setup now appears in the form of a double row of attached chairs, a desk with a blackboard behind it.* MR. HIBBETTS, *a balding, bespectacled fellow, is at the desk. He removes his glasses and polishes them, blinking his eyes in the glare. Then he turns and writes on the blackboard the name Liam McTeague. Through this,* MOLLIE *and* FRANK *have come in. There are apparently other fathers and daughters attending the class, but they are not seen.* MOLLIE *tries to snag two seats in the back row, but somebody apparently gets there first. She captures two seats in the middle for herself and* FRANK *and gestures someone else to the seat in front of them. She and* FRANK *settle down.* FRANK *takes a good look at* HIBBETTS *and then looks doubtfully at* MOLLIE, *who looks straight ahead.* HIBBETTS *"ers" constantly when he speaks. It's not that the fathers make him nervous; he does it all the time*)

HIBBETTS (*With a toothy smile*) On behalf of the English Department ... er ... I should like to extend a welcome to ... er ... those of you who have come to observe ... er ... and we hope you will not only observe ... er ... but also participate. If there are any questions which you would like to ask, please feel free to ... er ... throw them at me and I'll do my best to ... er ... field them. (HIBBETTS *feels that this figure of speech has made him one of the boys and he*

laughs. FRANK *manages to bare his teeth in response and exchanges an uncomfortable look with* MOLLIE) Today I thought we might pursue our study of the . . . er . . . poetry of Liam McTeague. As I said the last time we met . . . er . . . unfortunately McTeague, one of the . . . finest of the moderns, seems to be known . . . by the general public more for his . . . er . . . drinking habits than for his . . . er . . . exquisite poetry. Although . . . er . . . in fairness, McTeague has done more than his . . . er . . . share in . . . *projecting* this image. As for example when asked by the BBC to read the following poem . . . er . . . on the air . . . he arrived somewhat under the . . . er . . . influence of the . . . er . . . grape and . . . er . . . completely rewrote it . . . and was cut off in the middle. (*This ends on a note of surprise.* FRANK *exchanges another look with* MOLLIE) Well, enough of that. Here is, I suppose, what one might call the . . . er . . . watered-down version of that . . . er . . . poem. (*He laughs again, feeling he has made a joke.* FRANK *rests his chin on the palm of his hand and does his best to look intelligent and interested*) It is called "Life, Death, and a Small Installment Due." (*He opens a book and reads*)
"Kickingly, pantingly squallingly
Outwardly thrusting
In pain and shock and disbelief
Hopingly, graspingly, aspiringly
Trustfully demanding
Though all prerecorded
Synchronized and sealed
Impermanently permanent
Yet scrimpingly, sparingly, clingingly
Scheming and striving
For millions and monuments
Marbles and millstones

Negating the ultimate
All interest canceled
Repossessed."
Liverpool, 1956.
> (FRANK's *chin slips out of the palm of his hand*)

FRANK (*Whispering to* MOLLIE)   Well . . . that last part's clear.

MOLLIE   Sh!
> (HIBBETTS' *birdlike glance picks him up*)

HIBBETTS   Did you want to comment, Mr. . . . er . . . This *is* your father, isn't it, Mollie?

MOLLIE (*Nervously*)   Yes, Mr. Hibbetts.

HIBBETTS   Did you want to comment, Mr. Michaelson?

FRANK   Er . . . no . . . er . . . not particularly.

HIBBETTS   Well, did the poem have any impact?

FRANK   Oh, yes, yes. Definitely.

HIBBETTS   I see. (*To the other nonexistent class members*) Any other comments? (*Apparently there are none. He falls back on* FRANK *to keep the discussion alive*) Mr. . . . er . . . Michaelson, I can't help feeling that you . . . er . . . *did* have . . . er . . . something to say, and I wish you wouldn't feel . . . er . . . inhibited. Just feel . . . er . . . free to speak. For example, what . . . er . . . image did the poem suggest to you, if . . . er . . . any?

FRANK (*Leans forward*)   Well, it suggested the image of a fellow who was having quite a bit of trouble with the

Household Finance Corporation. (MOLLIE *is clasping her hands together and has her face turned away.* FRANK *looks hopefully at* HIBBETTS) Am I on the right track?

HIBBETTS (*Carefully*) I don't think McTeague has ever . . . er . . . been evaluated in such . . . er . . . practical, everyday terms . . .

FRANK Well, I'm not really a very good judge of this sort of thing. I think I agree with—I think it was Bernard Shaw who said: "Every man should be a poet at twenty-one, and any man who's still a poet at thirty is a first-class fool."
(MOLLIE, *in pain, sinks down in her seat and covers her face with her hand*)

HIBBETTS (*Polishing his glasses*) As I recall, Shaw said that about Socialists.

FRANK Oh, no. Shaw was a Socialist to the end. He said that about poets. How old is this McTeague?

HIBBETTS I'm not quite sure. I'll have to look that up.
(*He consults his book*)

MOLLIE (*Hissing in* FRANK's *ear*) Daddy, Daddy, Mr. Hibbetts writes poetry!

FRANK How old is he?

MOLLIE Old enough to flunk me.

FRANK (*Whispering*) Gee, I'm sorry, honey. Why didn't you tell me?

MOLLIE Who thought you'd get involved in a . . .
(FRANK *realizes that* MOLLIE *is upset. He thinks a*

94

moment, then raises his hand. HIBBETTS *doesn't see this.*
FRANK *waves his hand in the air. Still no effect on*
HIBBETTS)

FRANK   Oh, Mr. Hibbetts ...

HIBBETTS   Yes, Mr. Michaelson?

FRANK   (*Rises*)   Don't bother looking that up. As I recall,
you're quite right. Shaw *did* say that about Socialists, not
poets.

HIBBETTS (*Relieved*)   Oh, thank you.

FRANK   (*In a whisper to* MOLLIE; *their two heads together*) I
think I fixed that, don't you?

MOLLIE   Yes, Daddy. (*Realizing* HIBBETTS *is looking at them*)
Shhhh.

HIBBETTS   Mollie, if you ... er ... have any comments to
make ... er ... I wish you wouldn't keep them in the ...
er ... bosom of the family but would ... er ... let us all
share them.

MOLLIE   Well, I didn't really ...

HIBBETTS   Oh? McTeague has no impact on you whatever?

MOLLIE   (*Something in* HIBBETTS' *tone irritates her*) Well,
frankly, Mr. Hibbetts, I find McTeague empty.

HIBBETTS   Well ... er ... perhaps that's ... er ... what he
wants you to feel.

MOLLIE But I just don't feel *anything*. In every one of his poems, at least the ones I've read, he seems to find all of existence so utterly futile, as if life were just . . . an intermission between . . . two shocking events, birth and death. Which, I suppose, is why he's always drinking or rotting, or throwing his life away, or whatever. He seems completely preoccupied with the obvious fact that from the day we're born we're all rushing toward death. Life is full of so many beautiful things which he seems to ignore entirely. (*A pause for breath*) In other words, I'm in complete agreement with the previous speaker!

(FRANK *beams at her. Together he and* MOLLIE *get up and come downstage as the classroom moves off. They are now on the green of the campus*)

FRANK Gee, Mollie, I thought you were just great.

MOLLIE Thanks, Daddy. (*Thoughtfully*) You know, Mr. Hibbetts looked different today—I'm not even sure he's a good teacher.

FRANK He's a good teacher. He's fine. (*Looks around, delighted with his view of the campus. With enthusiasm*) Where do we go now?

MOLLIE Medieval History.

FRANK You'll be glad to hear I don't know a damn thing about medieval history. (*Thoughtfully*) Of course, I don't know anything about modern poetry either, still . . .
(*They stroll across stage together*)

MOLLIE After Medieval History, there's an art exhibition with the usual lecturer. Then there's a lunch with the Dean of

Women, then an archery contest on the lawn. After that, there's the father-daughter ping-pong tournament. Linda Lehman's father defaulted, so I rushed down and got their place for us.

FRANK   Well, come on. Let's get going.

MOLLIE   How do you feel?

FRANK   Just great.

MOLLIE   You know, sometimes I think the wrong Michaelson is going to college.
(*She takes his arm and they go off the stage. As the dormitory comes on, lit for evening, a chorus of girls' voices is heard singing the Hawthorne Alma Mater to the tune of "O Tannenbaum"*)

GIRLS' VOICES   (*Singing*)
"O Hawthorne, O Hawthorne,
Beside the shining waters.
O Hawthorne, O Hawthorne,
We're proud to be your daughters.
We pledge our faith, our honor true,
With grateful hearts we sing to you.
O Hawthorne, O Hawthorne,
We're proud to be your daughters."
(*In the course of the song,* MOLLIE *comes into the room, followed by* FRANK, *who staggers slightly*)

MOLLIE   It's five-thirty, Daddy. You haven't got time to go back to the hotel. I told you.

FRANK   Which bed is yours?

97

MOLLIE This one, right here. (*He collapses onto it, unaware that he is lying on a stuffed animal*) Now, Daddy, you can't pass out on me.

FRANK (*Not convinced*) Can't I?

MOLLIE Well there's still the banquet and two one-act plays by Ionesco . . .

FRANK (*Feebly*) Two?

MOLLIE Two. And then the dance.

FRANK Where's that held? In the infirmary? Mollie, get me a drink, will you?

MOLLIE Sure, Daddy. Be right back. And remember—don't pass out!
(*He shows every intention of doing just that as she goes.* SARAH *comes into the room and looks at him*)

SARAH Oh, it's Mr. Michaelson. I'm Sarah Walker.

FRANK (*Sadly, trying to rise*) I wish you hadn't done that. Now I have to get up.

SARAH (*Sits on the other bed*) No. Please don't. I understand.
(MOLLIE *dashes back in with a glass of water*)

MOLLIE Here, Daddy. (*Then she crosses to the desk*) Hi, Sarah.

FRANK (*Sits up and takes the glass*) Thank you, dear.

SARAH I hear you got to the finals in the ping-pong tournament.

FRANK   Yes, and we'd have won, if we hadn't got that bad call. (*He has a swallow, then sputters with indignation*) Water! Don't they *teach* you anything at this college?

MOLLIE   Daddy, you can get kicked out of school for . . . (*Changing*) Sarah, where's your mouth wash?

SARAH   On the book shelf . . . (MOLLIE *goes to the door*) . . . behind Dewey's *Moral Principles of Education*.

MOLLIE   I'll only be a minute.
(*She rushes out.* FRANK *lies back and closes his eyes*)

FRANK   Drink or no drink, I don't think I'm going to be able to make it. My back is killing me.

SARAH   (*Rises, crosses to the other bed*) Excuse me, Mr. Michaelson.
(*She reaches under the small of his back, pulls out the stuffed animal and hands it to him*)

FRANK   Oh, hello, Pluto. I gave him to Mollie on her fourth birthday. He's the only one of us who hasn't changed.
(MOLLIE *is back with a large bottle labeled "Mouth Wash"*)

MOLLIE   (*Giving* FRANK *the bottle*) Here you are, Daddy.
(*He pours a hefty slug into his glass. She takes the bottle and sits*)

FRANK   (*Sniffs the aroma appreciatively*) Aaaaah. Well, I'm being kicked out tomorrow anyway so—cheers!
(*He downs the drink.* ADELE *sticks her head in the doorway*)

ADELE Mollie . . .
(*She gestures to indicate she'd like* MOLLIE *to come out*)

MOLLIE Excuse me a minute, Daddy.
(*She puts the bottle on the floor.* ADELE *and* MOLLIE *go*)

FRANK Mollie said your father didn't come this weekend.

SARAH Not one of them. (*Leaning forward*) I thought I wouldn't mind, but I do.

FRANK What are you planning to do when you . . .

SARAH Graduate? (*He nods*) Oh, take my master's, then my Ph.D. Then I'll teach. I'm not going out into the real world. Everybody out there is miserable. I'm staying right here. Is that a very young idea?

FRANK I understand what you mean. Everybody drinks too much or eats too much or thinks about himself too much.
(*He takes a sip*)

SARAH Or sleeps around too much.

FRANK Oh, don't go by John O'Hara novels. That's mostly wishful thinking—(*He drinks*)—among the people I know, anyway. (FRANK *gropes for the bottle.* SARAH *gets it and pours him another*) Thank you. You really want to teach?

SARAH Oh, yes. I know it's a surprise to everybody, but I get very good grades. (MOLLIE *comes back into the room, looking disturbed.* SARAH *senses it and turns to go*) Well, thank you, Mr. Michaelson.

FRANK What for?

SARAH For being a listener. (*She starts out*) Well, have a ball. I hear the kitchen is going all out to serve what they consider a Roman banquet—grape juice and fried chicken. (*She exits*)

MOLLIE You can freshen up in the bathroom. (*Indicating the direction*) I'm going to wear the blue you gave me for Christmas.

FRANK Good. I like that dress.
    (FRANK *disappears in the direction of the bathroom.* MOLLIE *kicks off her shoes and starts changing to her blue dress*)

FRANK'S VOICE You know, Mollie, frankly last night I had some doubts about this. Took me quite a while to fall asleep. That Clancy Sussman is pretty hard to digest. Anyway, today was marvelous. Seeing this place and going to class with you and being around young people. Even meeting Liam McTeague for the first time. (*Intoning*) "Inwardly. Outwardly. Kickingly. Pantingly." (*Then singing*) "Inwardly, outwardly, kickingly, pantingly." It made me feel it was all good. That it wasn't a mistake. I can't wait to get home and tell your mother what a wonderful . . .

MOLLIE (*Cutting him off, almost in tears*) Oh, Daddy!
    (FRANK *appears*)

FRANK Yes, Mollie?

MOLLIE Nothing, Daddy.

FRANK Nothing?

MOLLIE Can you zip me up?

FRANK (*Carrying his coat and knotting his tie*) Sure. Say, I like that dress. I have good taste in women's clothes. I don't know why, but I have.

(*He zips her up and fastens a hook*)

MOLLIE (*Turns to* FRANK) Daddy . . .

FRANK Yes, Mollie?

MOLLIE You remember I wrote you about that fellowship to go abroad this summer?

FRANK With the State Department. Of course.

MOLLIE That's what Adele wanted to see me about. She just saw the list in her sister's office. And my name wasn't on it.

FRANK (*Clears his throat*) I'm sorry.

MOLLIE So am I.

FRANK Only because you wanted it. It really isn't important.

MOLLIE Oh, yes it is. It's very important.

FRANK (*Thinks a moment*) It's just a summer in Europe doing some sort of paper work which may or may not be socially significant. So what? (*He turns her to face him*) If you want to go to Europe this summer . . .

MOLLIE It isn't that.

FRANK But I can send you. And I think you'd learn a lot more going around on a bicycle.

MOLLIE   That has nothing to do with it. (*She shakes her head*) I failed, don't you see? (*She turns*) The first time in my life I wanted something and I didn't get it. And you can't give it to me . . . you can't. (*Being relentless with herself*) I thought I was so sharp . . . I'd walk in and they'd fall all over themselves to get me. (*She sits on the bed*) I just got a picture of what I must have looked like. Even you wouldn't have given me the job.

FRANK (*Sits next to* MOLLIE)   Oh, honey . . .

MOLLIE   Daddy, I'm so far away from what you want. What you must think of me . . .

FRANK (*Takes her chin in his hand*)   What I think of you? Mollie, let's get one thing straight. If they sent me the news that you had burned down the college and murdered the dean, I would forgive you. It's what you think of yourself that matters.

MOLLIE (*With her head on* FRANK's *shoulder*)   I'm so ashamed.

FRANK   If you can see that, it's the beginning of getting an education.

MOLLIE   Are you shrinking my head?

FRANK   A little. Come on now. (*Rises*) We're going to a dance tonight, and we'll be the coolest couple on the floor. Here . . . (*Offering a handkerchief*) Dry your eyes.
  (MOLLIE *manages a smile, rises, goes to the mirror and looks at herself.* FRANK *gets her evening purse from the desk*)

MOLLIE   God, I look awful.

FRANK (*Looking over her shoulder at the mirror*) Hideous, but you're my date and I'm stuck with you. I may not look like much myself, but I'll bet I'm the only father at Hawthorne College who's studied the rhumba for two solid years.

(*He offers his arm, and they exit grandly. The dormitory goes off. The campus fence appears, lit for day.* ALEX *is leaning against it, pretending to be reading. He looks off to the left, apparently waiting for someone. Then he looks to the right and sees someone coming. He goes to the other side of the fence, turns his back and reads, to avoid being seen. In a moment,* SARAH *comes on, accompanied by* 1ST FRESHMAN)

1ST FRESHMAN What was that author's name again?

SARAH Kafka.

1ST FRESHMAN (*Pretending great interest*) Mmmhmmm.

SARAH He wrote *Metamorphosis*. It's really a very strange story.

1ST FRESHMAN Oh, sure . . . *Metamorphosis*.

SARAH It's all about this man who wakes up one morning and finds out he's a cockroach.

1ST FRESHMAN Yeh.

SARAH And his family locks him in his room . . . What do you suppose Kafka means by that?
(*They walk across the stage together*)

1ST FRESHMAN Oh, I read that story. As I analyze it, aside from the fact that it's mortifying to have a cockroach in the family, this man had a sense of guilt because he was trying to displace his own father.

(*They stop*)

SARAH Then he really did it to himself?

IST FRESHMAN Conceivably. (*Pause*) By the way, what are you doing tonight?

SARAH Why?

IST FRESHMAN Well, I thought we could pursue this discussion further and see where it gets us.

(*They go off.* ALEX *looks after them, then evidently sees someone coming. He moves to the other side of the fence and again pretends to be engrossed in his book.* MOLLIE *comes on slowly from the left. She is in a sweater and skirt, and carries some books and a small sheaf of green leaves. She walks right past* ALEX *without seeing him. This brings him to his feet*)

ALEX Hello.

MOLLIE (*Bemused*) Oh, hello, Alex.

ALEX (*Looks at her curiously*) Something the matter?

MOLLIE No. I'm just a million miles away. We don't have spring in California, you see. Aren't they lovely?

ALEX What? (*She indicates the leaves*) The leaves? Oh, yes, yes, they're beautiful.

MOLLIE The woods are full of wild flowers, but it seemed a shame to pick them.

ALEX (*After a blank look at her, he sits on the fence*) Can we talk? Or are you in a hurry?

MOLLIE (*Leaning on the fence*) Oh, no. I'm never in a hurry. People hurry too much—through life. (*Quoting*) "The complexities of civilization stand in the way of significant living."

ALEX That rings a bell. It's a quote.

MOLLIE Is there *anything* you don't know?

ALEX Oh, so much . . . There's so little I know outside of books—it's driving me nuts.

MOLLIE Everybody has his problems.

ALEX And you're solving yours by communing with nature. (*He snaps his fingers*) I've got it! Thoreau! (*Looking at her*) Are you going through that bit now?

MOLLIE What bit?

ALEX The Thoreau bit. You know, living the simple life, eating nuts and berries, playing with the pickerel in the pond . . .

MOLLIE (*Annoyed*) The pickerel in the pond! Honestly, you leap to the most ridiculous conclusions. (*She moves toward ALEX; he backs away a few steps*) Just because I happened to quote Thoreau! Life isn't just one thing or another. It's a combination of things.

ALEX (*Sorry he started this*) All right.

MOLLIE You intellectualize so much. You put labels on everything.

ALEX All right, Mollie, all right.
(MOLLIE *walks away from him, stops, with her back to him*)

MOLLIE (*Stiffly*) What did you want to see me about?

ALEX (*Raising his hands helplessly*) I have the feeling if I tell you now, you'll cheer, maybe.

MOLLIE (*Turns*) I might. What is it?

ALEX I came to say goodbye.

MOLLIE Oh.

ALEX I've finished my master's, and I'm not coming back.

MOLLIE Now, why did you think I'd want to cheer because you came to say goodbye? That's a terrible thing to say.

ALEX Mollie, that's the story of our relationship. I always say the wrong thing to you.

MOLLIE Are your prospects good ones?

ALEX Yes. All of them. Very.

MOLLIE That's very nice for you.

ALEX I don't know why I'm hostile. I don't really mean to be. It's just my manner. Last time I saw you we got into a violent argument about Italian movies. I couldn't care less about Italian movies!

MOLLIE Well, you don't really need that manner any more, Alex. It's all right for someone like me, who's all wasted motion, just floundering about . . .

ALEX *(Gently)* Mollie . . .

MOLLIE Please! I can't stand sympathy. *(A pause)* I'm sure I'll hear about you—or read about you.
(He takes her hand)

ALEX Mollie, let's have dinner tonight.

MOLLIE I can't. I take my last final tomorrow, and I've got to cram all night. Contemporary History. I'm having an awful time with Contemporary History.

ALEX Tomorrow night, then.

MOLLIE I'm taking the plane home tomorrow afternoon. *(Silence for a moment; they drop hands)* Goodbye, Alex. Thank you.

ALEX Goodbye, Mollie. *(He starts off, stops)* Goddammit, goodbye!
(He goes off. MOLLIE is alone. She starts to go off, changes her mind, stops and looks after ALEX. She hesitates, appears about to call after him, then shakes her head. She sighs and goes off. The lights go out slowly. There is the sound of airplanes.)
(At stage left, the lights go on; a barbecue has appeared, its back to the audience. ANNE, in slacks and a shirt, is fanning the fire. At center stage, a garden table and chairs and a chaise longue are seen. LIZ comes out of the house, looking somewhat grown up, with her hair

*pulled back off her forehead with a band, and sunglasses
on. She wears tight pants and a flapping shirt)*

LIZ   How's the fire doing, Mom?

ANNE   Fine. (*Looking around in the still-bright light*) Oh, I
hate the summers in California. I wonder if it's raining any
place. I'd like to go there.

LIZ (*Sits and takes off her glasses*) Not me. I'm having the
most marvelous summer.

ANNE   Are you, dear? I'm glad. (FRANK *comes out, evidently
in a grouchy mood; crosses to chaise longue, sits and opens
his newspaper*) What was on the news?

FRANK   "Good night, Chet." "Good night, David." (*Reading
the paper*) Those two are such a comfort to each other.
Where's her Royal Highness?

ANNE   Incommunicado.

LIZ   She's in her room. She's got a sign on her door: "*Ne frappez pas à cette porte.*"

ANNE   Resting?

LIZ (*Shakes her head*)   I thought I heard her working on that
crazy stenotype machine she's so goofy about.

FRANK   I'd like to *frappez* on her ...

ANNE   Frank!

LIZ (*Importantly*) Mom, Daddy, there's something I want to talk to you about. (*Reacting to her own tone*) Gosh! Sounds like I'm having a baby!

FRANK Are you?

LIZ (*Gets up*) No, of course not.

FRANK Well, don't scare us like that, will you?

LIZ Don't worry about that. I'm a great believer in planned parenthood. What I want to talk to you about is . . .
(*The phone has started to ring*)

ANNE That's the phone.

FRANK Would you get it, honey?

LIZ Oh, sure, sure. Don't go 'way.
(*She goes into the house*)

FRANK (*Gets up and crosses to* ANNE) Look, I don't want anybody to get the wrong impression. (*Belligerently*) It's perfectly all right with me if Mollie quits college. There's nothing wrong with her becoming a court stenographer. It's a perfectly good job.

ANNE And it pays very well.

FRANK Also, it's high time somebody else brought some money into this house.
(LIZ *comes back*)

ANNE Who was that on the phone?

LIZ A boy, for Mollie.

ANNE Did you *frappez* on her *porte?*

LIZ No. I yellayed up the stairs.

FRANK (*Takes a good look at her*) What are you dressed up as anyway? You know, if I had wanted a son, I'd have had one!

LIZ Daddy, I've been wearing this all summer.

FRANK Then it's about time you changed.

LIZ Well, I have something to say first.

FRANK I'm sure you have. (*Brusquely*) I left two drinks on the bar. Would you bring them out here?

LIZ Oh, sure. (*Going*) I wish Lincoln had freed the children, too!
　　(*She exits*)

FRANK (*Inspecting the fire*) Who built that fire?

ANNE I did. Why?

FRANK Nothing! It's fine.
　　(*He stomps back to the chaise*)

ANNE Frank . . . (*Sitting on a chair; he looks at her*) Let go. You have to let go.

FRANK That's exactly what I'm doing. I'm letting go. I have cut the umbilical cord!
　　(*He accompanies that with a cutting gesture*)

ANNE *You* have? That's very interesting.

FRANK Well, you know what I mean.
 (MOLLIE's *voice is heard*)

MOLLIE'S VOICE Daddy!

FRANK Yes, Mollie.

MOLLIE'S VOICE Can we handle one extra for dinner? Is there enough steak?

FRANK Yes. Sure.

MOLLIE'S VOICE Good.

FRANK Who? Who's coming? (*No answer*) She's gone.

ANNE (*Comfortably*) Oh, she'll have to introduce him. We'll all be eating at the same table.
 (LIZ *marches out, carrying two drinks. She hands one to* ANNE *and one to* FRANK)

LIZ (*Grimly*) Here's your drink, Mom. Here's yours, Daddy. Now will both of you please look at me? (*They look surprised*) I am your daughter Elizabeth. I have been trying to say something. It isn't very important, but I'd like to say it!

FRANK What are you being so dramatic about? If you have something to say, say it.

LIZ (*Taking a deep breath; to* ANNE) I have a message for you from Emmett Whitmyer.

FRANK That little bastard.

LIZ (*Crosses to* FRANK, *puts her hand on his shoulder*) Yes. He has an idea you feel that way, and he wonders if he can come over and show you how much he's changed.

FRANK Who cares whether he's changed or not? Mollie's not interested in him.

LIZ He's not interested in Mollie.

FRANK (*Looks up at her, realizing what she means*) Oh, come on!

LIZ (*Flaring up*) What's so wrong with that? Everybody in this house is so busy thinking about Mollie, they don't seem to realize that I'm growing up, too! (*To* ANNE) It doesn't occur to you that I might have some problems. But if you don't want to discuss them, that's quite all right with me. It doesn't matter in the least! (*Taking a few steps toward the house*) I'm perfectly capable of handling things myself! So you just go on worrying about Mollie. But remember, it won't be long before *I* go away to school, too! I mean, let's get things in proper focus, shall we?
(*She stalks off.* FRANK *stares after her*)

FRANK Maybe the British are right. They don't try to understand children. They just send them away as early as possible.

ANNE (*Gets up and goes to the barbecue*) Oh, the hell with it. My mother and father never understood me—and I enjoyed it enormously. The hell with them.
(MOLLIE *comes in carrying her stenotype machine*)

MOLLIE Hi.

FRANK (*Without looking up from his paper*) Hello.

ANNE Well, aren't you dressed up!

MOLLIE Do I look all right?

ANNE Lovely.

FRANK Who's coming to dinner?

MOLLIE (*Sits*) A boy from Harvard.

ANNE Isn't that nice?

FRANK (*Reading the paper*) What's so nice about it? I'm not so sure about Harvard as the rest of the country is.

MOLLIE (*Trying to make him understand*) But this boy is ... (*He doesn't look up from the paper; she abandons the attempt*) Does anybody want to give me some dictation?

FRANK (*Slaps down the newspaper and gets up*) I'll give you some dictation. Michaelson versus Michaelson.

ANNE Oh, the fight of the week. Pardon me.
(*She goes into the house*)

FRANK (*Pacing upstage, as* MOLLIE *works at the machine*) Case between Frank Michaelson, hereinafter referred to as the plaintiff, and Mollie Michaelson, hereinafter referred to as the defendant. (MOLLIE *throws him a look. He rattles his speech off at breakneck speed.* MOLLIE *tries to follow, then stops*) The plaintiff wishes the court to recognize that his case is a simple one. He stipulates that the defendant has been making a damn fool of herself and ought to go back to school and make full use of the brains that God was good enough to give her ... Have you got that?

MOLLIE   I got as far as "damn fool."

FRANK   (*Crosses to the table*)   Then you got it! Mollie, you have horsepower. You and that machine make as much sense as a ... a Diesel engine pulling a kiddie car!

MOLLIE   (*Turns front*)   Daddy, don't you realize you have an image of me that doesn't exist? Haven't I proved to you in the last two years that I'm none of the things you want me to be? And college! Your idea of college! That's the biggest riot of all. It's a lot of "will you" or "won't you" or "do you" or "don't you" or "I hope I'm not the first, am I?" Think about that for a while. You talk about it as if it's something. It's nothing. It's just a very small tragedy in a very small life.
    (*The doorbell rings in the house.* LIZ's *voice is heard*)

LIZ's VOICE   Mollie! The doorbell.

MOLLIE   (*Gets up*)   Would you get it, please?
    (FRANK *moves left slowly*)

LIZ's VOICE   I can't. I'm changing.

ANNE's VOICE   I'll get it, dear.

LIZ's VOICE   Somebody in this house doesn't approve of the way I dress!

FRANK   (*A gesture of futility*)   I'll go see about the steaks.
    (*He exits left.* MOLLIE *moves nervously left of the table, smoothing her dress and her hair. She waits a moment,*

then starts toward the house. ANNE *appears, showing* ALEX *out to the garden*)

ANNE Mollie's expecting you.

ALEX I'm glad.

ANNE She's right out here.
(*She exits*)

ALEX Thank you, Mrs. Michaelson. (*He comes out into the garden. He and* MOLLIE *look at each other for a moment*) Hello, Mollie.

MOLLIE Alex, I'm so glad to see you. What are you doing in Los Angeles?

ALEX Well, I came here on impulse. I've changed my whole character now. I'm living by impulse rather than by reason.

MOLLIE Let me know if it works.
(*She sits*)

ALEX I'm on my way to San Francisco.

MOLLIE By way of Los Angeles?

ALEX Yes. (MOLLIE *looks away*) I came to see you. (MOLLIE *looks at* ALEX; *there is a pause.* ALEX *sits*) I'm going to Stanford. I've got a teaching fellowship there.

MOLLIE Congratulations. You came to see me?

ALEX I wrote you a lot of letters, Mollie. An awful lot of them.

MOLLIE (*Looks at* ALEX) You did? (*She looks down*) I waited for them, but they never came.

ALEX I tore them all up. I even wrote a speech . . . But I'm not going to use it. By the way, are you married, or engaged, or anything?

MOLLIE I'm not married or engaged, and I'm not quite sure what "or anything" means.

ALEX (*Gets up, has trouble finding words, finally turns to face* MOLLIE) Mollie, let's be conventional.

MOLLIE All right. Let's.

ALEX If I stick around the next couple of weeks before I go to Stanford—will you give me some time?

MOLLIE Yes . . .

ALEX You will?

MOLLIE Lots of time, Alex.

ALEX I think I'll read that speech after all. (*Takes it out, reads*) "Despite many rebuffs, I think about Miss Mollie Michaelson every day, with the following results: a) loss of sleep; b) loss of appetite; c) loss of temper; d) loss of driver's license." (MOLLIE *laughs; he looks up from his paper*) I went through two red lights. I was thinking about Miss Mollie Michaelson. Shall I go on?

MOLLIE No. I get the idea.

ALEX Oh, Mollie.

MOLLIE (*Gets up, takes a few steps; then*) I think we're going to have a wonderful two weeks.

ALEX (*Taking her hands*) Mollie, I have a great idea. Why don't you transfer to Stanford and finish your education up there? It's really a hell of a school.

MOLLIE I've finished my education. I've quit college, I'm going to become a court stenographer.

ALEX You're kidding.

MOLLIE No. My father is absolutely furious.

ALEX I should think so. (FRANK *comes out with the steaks on a platter covered with waxed paper. Neither of them sees him*) It's the most idiotic thing I ever heard of. You might want to go to South Africa and teach, or get a job with *Time* magazine, or— You need a degree for that. Of course, you can be perfectly well educated without a degree, but why shut those doors on yourself? Who knows what you'll wind up doing?

MOLLIE Then you think it's a mistake?

ALEX I most certainly do. With your capabilities? With your potential?

MOLLIE You know, nobody ever quite put it to me in those terms before.
     (FRANK *has the look of a man who has been pole-axed He stands stunned for a moment*)

FRANK   Good God!
>   (*He turns and heaves the steaks at the barbecue, as lights go out.*)
>   (*The airplane noises are heard. The lights come up on a steel-link fence leading to the plane. The* AIRPORT CLERK *is checking tickets for imaginary passengers and waving them through the gate.* ANNE *and* LIZ *come on from left, laden down with* LIZ's *possessions.* LIZ *looks very like* MOLLIE *when she first went off to school—quite grown up, in traveling suit and hat.* LIZ *puts a large shapeless bag down and crosses the stage in search of her father.* ANNE *follows*)

LIZ   Where's Daddy? If he doesn't get here right away, I'll be gone.

ANNE   He probably had trouble finding a parking spot.

LIZ   What about that speech about how I have to help change the world? I have that coming to me.

ANNE   Yes, dear, it's part of the course.
>   (FRANK *comes rushing in and joins them*)

FRANK   I thought you were still at the counter.

ANNE   We couldn't wait. They announced the flight.

FRANK   (*Takes* LIZ's *arm and strolls with her companionably, speaking earnestly*)   Liz, I want you to listen to me. Now, more than ever, the world is facing the challenge of new ideas. Radcliffe, in its own way, is in a class with great schools like . . .
>   (LIZ *evidently sees somebody going past, leaves her father*)

LIZ Hi, Barbara . . . Daddy, Mom, this is Mr. and Mrs. Tre-back. Barbara's going to Hawthorne. (*There is an exchange of greetings*) Have you got your seat yet?
> (LIZ *and* Barbara *move off to the left for a private conversation*)

FRANK Our other daughter went there for two years. She just switched to Stanford . . . Oh, no. She loved Hawthorne. But you see, her fiancé is a professor at Stanford.

ANNE A professor!

FRANK (*Ignores that*) And . . . well . . . (MOLLIE *and* ALEX *come in from right, arm-in-arm, and all wrapped up in each other. They are dressed for travel*) There they are. See what I mean? (ANNE *excuses herself and joins* MOLLIE *and* ALEX. FRANK *speaks in a confidential tone*) You know, of the two, Liz being more balanced, might just possibly be . . .
> (*He taps the side of his head sagely*)

LIZ You'd better get in line.

FRANK (*Waving goodbye*) Well, see you at Christmas . . . (*Calling after them*) Oh, by the way, don't miss father-daughter weekend at Hawthorne—a little expensive, but you'll have a ball! (LIZ *is also waving goodbye. He turns her around to face him. She listens obediently.* ANNE *rejoins them*) Now, Liz, I want you to take full advantage of the Harvard faculty . . .
> (EMMETT *comes into scene looking very grown up, he thinks, and a little too Ivy League—raincoat slung over one shoulder, small suitcase in hand*)

ANNE Oh, Emmett.

LIZ Hi, Emmett.

EMMETT Hello, Mrs. Michaelson. Good evening, sir. Well, it certainly has been a long time.

FRANK Not long enough for . . .

ANNE (*Cutting in*) Are you on this flight, too?

EMMETT Yes. Don't worry about Elizabeth, sir. I'll keep an eye on her for you.

FRANK Thank you. (LIZ *and* EMMETT *drift off left for a whispered consultation*) Just what I need to guarantee a good night's sleep.
    (LIZ *rejoins them, leaving* EMMETT)

LIZ Daddy, you don't have to have any fears about Emmett. I've got him completely under control.

ANNE They're loading, dear.

LIZ I'm going! Goodbye, everybody!
    (*She kisses her mother and father, and her possessions are piled into her arms in a flurry of ad libs. She kisses* MOLLIE, *then offers her hand to* ALEX, *who gives her a fraternal kiss on the cheek. She throws a look of blissful envy at Mollie, then goes through gate. They wave and call after her a final salvo of "goodbyes" and "don't forget to write." As* LIZ *passes* EMMETT *at the left end of the fence, she stops and points imperiously to her large bag.* EMMETT *picks it up and swings it over the fence to her. All watch as she goes off.* EMMETT *now picks up his own small bag, and proceeds in a very dignified, somewhat martial manner to the ticket taker. He hands*

over his ticket, turns to exchange a bland smile with
MOLLIE, *and he goes.* FRANK *and* ANNE *now turn to*
MOLLIE *and* ALEX)

FRANK What gate is your plane?

ALEX It hasn't been announced. We have an hour yet.

MOLLIE Look, there's really no reason for you two to hang
around the airport all that time.
(ANNE *throws a look at* FRANK *to see what effect that
had on him*)

FRANK No...I...I guess not. Well, goodbye.
(*He shakes* ALEX's *hand*)

MOLLIE Goodbye, Mom. Goodbye, Daddy. (*There is another
exchange of kisses, a little stiff and formal, after which
they break apart, and* MOLLIE *and* ALEX *start off right.* FRANK
and ANNE *stand and watch them go. They are almost off,
when* MOLLIE *stops and looks back at her parents*) Daddy!
Mom! (*She runs back to them and throws her arms around*
FRANK's *neck. They break apart and she puts one arm on*
ANNE's *shoulder, the other on* FRANK's) San Francisco is
only fifty-five minutes away.

FRANK We know. (*Smiling at her*) Just around the corner.
(MOLLIE *nods, then goes slowly to rejoin* ALEX; *they go off.*
FRANK *and* ANNE *stand for a moment in silence*) Annie, looking back, I can see now, it was just a question of growing
up. That's all it was.

ANNE (*Links her arm through his*) You know there were
times, Frank, when I never thought you would.
(*He turns and looks at her*)
                    Curtain